CALIFORNIA **INTEGRATED**

elevate science

SAVVAS
LEARNING COMPANY

AUTHORS

You're an author!

As you write in this science book, your answers and personal discoveries will be recorded for you to keep, making this book unique to you. That is why you are one of the primary authors of this book.

✏️ **In the space below, print your name, school, town, and state. Then write a short autobiography that includes your interests and accomplishments.**

YOUR NAME ....

SCHOOL ....

TOWN, STATE ....

AUTOBIOGRAPHY ....

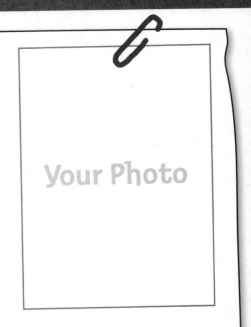

Your Photo

ISBN-13: 978-1-418-31045-5
ISBN-10:   1-418-31045-X
4

Program Authors

ZIPPORAH MILLER, Ed.D.
Coordinator for K-12 Science Programs, Anne Arundel County Public Schools
Dr. Zipporah Miller currently serves as the Senior Manager for Organizational Learning with the Anne Arundel County Public School System. Prior to that she served as the K-12 Coordinator for science in Anne Arundel County. She conducts national training to science stakeholders on the Next Generation Science Standards. Dr. Miller also served as the Associate Executive Director for Professional Development Programs and conferences at the National Science Teachers Association (NSTA) and served as a reviewer during the development of Next Generation Science Standards. Dr. Miller holds a doctoral degree from the University of Maryland College Park, a master's degree in school administration and supervision from Bowie State University and a bachelor's degree from Chadron State College.

MICHAEL J. PADILLA, Ph.D.
Professor Emeritus, Eugene P. Moore School of Education, Clemson University, Clemson, South Carolina
Michael J. Padilla taught science in middle and secondary schools, has more than 30 years of experience educating middle-school science teachers, and served as one of the writers of the 1996 U.S. National Science Education Standards. In recent years Mike has focused on teaching science to English Language Learners. His extensive experience as Principal Investigator on numerous National Science Foundation and U.S. Department of Education grants resulted in more than $35 million in funding to improve science education. He served as president of the National Science Teachers Association, the world's largest science teaching organization, in 2005–6.

MICHAEL E. WYSESSION, Ph.D
Professor of Earth and Planetary Sciences, Washington University, St. Louis, Missouri
Author of more than 100 science and science education publications, Dr. Wysession was awarded the prestigious National Science Foundation Presidential Faculty Fellowship and Packard Foundation Fellowship for his research in geophysics, primarily focused on using seismic tomography to determine the forces driving plate tectonics. Dr. Wysession is also a leader in geoscience literacy and education; he is the chair of the Earth Science Literacy Initiative, the author of several popular video lectures on geology in the *Great Courses* series, and a lead writer of the *Next Generation Science Standards**.

REVIEWERS

Program Consultants

Carol Baker
Science Curriculum

Dr. Carol K. Baker is superintendent for Lyons Elementary K-8 School District in Lyons, Illinois. Prior to this, she was Director of Curriculum for Science and Music in Oak Lawn, Illinois. Before this she taught Physics and Earth Science for 18 years. In the recent past, Dr. Baker also wrote assessment questions for ACT (EXPLORE and PLAN), was elected president of the Illinois Science Teachers Association from 2011–2013, and served as a member of the Museum of Science and Industry (Chicago) advisory board. She is a writer of the Next Generation Science Standards. Dr. Baker received her B.S. in Physics and a science teaching certification. She completed her master's of Educational Administration (K-12) and earned her doctorate in Educational Leadership.

Jim Cummins
ELL

Dr. Cummins's research focuses on literacy development in multilingual schools and the role technology plays in learning across the curriculum. *Elevate Science* incorporates research-based principles for integrating language with the teaching of academic content based on Dr. Cummins's work.

Elfrieda Hiebert
Literacy

Dr. Hiebert, a former primary-school teacher, is President and CEO of TextProject, a non-profit aimed at providing open-access resources for instruction of beginning and struggling readers, She is also a research associate at the University of California Santa Cruz. Her research addresses how fluency, vocabulary, and knowledge can be fostered through appropriate texts, and her contributions have been recognized through awards such as the Oscar Causey Award for Outstanding Contributions to Reading Research (Literacy Research Association, 2015), Research to Practice award (American Educational Research Association, 2013), and the William S. Gray Citation of Merit Award for Outstanding Contributions to Reading Research (International Reading Association, 2008).

Content Reviewers

Alex Blom, Ph.D.
Associate Professor
Department Of Physical Sciences
Alverno College
Milwaukee, Wisconsin

Joy Branlund, Ph.D.
Department of Physical Science
Southwestern Illinois College
Granite City, Illinois

Judy Calhoun
Associate Professor
Physical Sciences
Alverno College
Milwaukee, Wisconsin

Stefan Debbert
Associate Professor of Chemistry
Lawrence University
Appleton, Wisconsin

Diane Doser
Professor
Department of Geological Sciences
University of Texas at El Paso
El Paso, Texas

Rick Duhrkopf, Ph.D.
Department of Biology
Baylor University
Waco, Texas

Jennifer Liang
University of Minnesota Duluth
Duluth, Minnesota

Heather Mernitz, Ph.D.
Associate Professor of Physical Sciences
Alverno College
Milwaukee, Wisconsin

Joseph McCullough, Ph.D.
Cabrillo College
Aptos, California

Katie M. Nemeth, Ph.D.
Assistant Professor
College of Science and Engineering
University of Minnesota Duluth
Duluth, Minnesota

Maik Pertermann
Department of Geology
Western Wyoming Community College
Rock Springs, Wyoming

Scott Rochette
Department of the Earth Sciences
The College at Brockport
 State University of New York
Brockport, New York

David Schuster
Washington University in St Louis
St. Louis, Missouri

Shannon Stevenson
Department of Biology
University of Minnesota Duluth
Duluth, Minnesota

Paul Stoddard, Ph.D.
Department of Geology and
 Environmental Geosciences
Northern Illinois University
DeKalb, Illinois

Nancy Taylor
American Public University
Charles Town, West Virginia

Teacher Reviewers

Rita Armstrong
Los Cerritos Middle School
Thousand Oaks, California

Tyler C. Britt, Ed.S.
Curriculum & Instructional
Practice Coordinator
Raytown Quality Schools
Raytown, Missouri

Holly Bowser
Barstow High School
Barstow, California

David Budai
Coachella Valley Unified School District
Coachella, California

A. Colleen Campos
Grandview High School
Aurora, Colorado

Jodi DeRoos
Mojave River Academy
Colton, California

Colleen Duncan
Moore Middle School
Redlands, California

Nicole Hawke
Westside Elementary
Thermal, California

Margaret Henry
Lebanon Junior High School
Lebanon, Ohio

Ashley Humphrey
Riverside Preparatory Elementary
Oro Grande, California

Adrianne Kilzer
Riverside Preparatory Elementary
Oro Grande, California

Danielle King
Barstow Unified School District
Barstow, California

Kathryn Kooyman
Riverside Preparatory Elementary
Oro Grande, California

Esther Leonard M.Ed. and L.M.T.
Gifted and Talented Implementation Specialist
San Antonio Independent School District
San Antonio, Texas

Diana M. Maiorca, M.Ed.
Los Cerritos Middle School
Thousand Oaks, California

Kevin J. Maser, Ed.D.
H. Frank Carey Jr/Sr High School
Franklin Square, New York

Corey Mayle
Brogden Middle School
Durham, North Carolina

Keith McCarthy
George Washington Middle School
Wayne, New Jersey

Rudolph Patterson
Cobalt Institute of Math and Science
Victorville, California

Yolanda O. Peña
John F. Kennedy Junior High School
West Valley City, Utah

Stacey Phelps
Mojave River Academy
Oro Grande, California

Susan Pierce
Bryn Mawr Elementary
Redlands Unified School District
Redlands, California

Cristina Ramos
Mentone Elementary School
Redlands Unified School District
Mentone, California

Mary Regis
Franklin Elementary School
Redlands, California

Bryna Selig
Gaithersburg Middle School
Gaithersburg, Maryland

Pat (Patricia) Shane, Ph.D.
STEM & ELA Education Consultant
Chapel Hill, North Carolina

Elena Valencia
Coral Mountain Academy
Coachella, California

Janelle Vecchio
Mission Elementary School
Redlands, California

Brittney Wells
Riverside Preparatory Elementary
Oro Grande, California

Kristina Williams
Sequoia Middle School
Newbury Park, California

Safety Reviewers

Douglas Mandt, M.S.
Science Education Consultant
Edgewood, Washington

Juliana Textley, Ph.D.
Author, NSTA books on school science safety
Adjunct Professor
Lesley University
Cambridge, Massachusetts

California Spotlight
Instructional Segment 4

TOPICS 9–11

The SMART Way to Track Wildlife

TOPIC 9 Waves

Investigative Phenomenon How can you model the behavior and properties of waves?

MS-PS4-1, MS-PS4-2

HANDS-ON LABS

и**Connect**
и**Investigate**
и**Demonstrate**

HANDS-ON LABS
uConnect
uInvestigate
uDemonstrate

California Spotlight

The SMART Way to Track Wildlife

HANDS-ON LABS

иConnect
иInvestigate
иDemonstrate

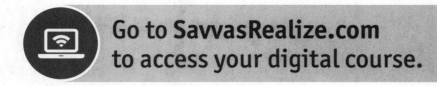

Go to SavvasRealize.com to access your digital course.

Elevate Science combines the best science narrative with a robust online program. Throughout the lessons, digital support is presented at point of use to enhance your learning experience.

Online Resources

Savvas Realize™ is your online science class. This digital-learning environment includes:

- Student eTEXT
- Instructor eTEXT
- Project-Based Learning
- Virtual Labs

- Interactivities
- Videos
- Assessments
- Study Tools
- and more!

Digital Features

 VIDEO

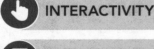 INTERACTIVITY

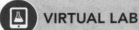 VIRTUAL LAB

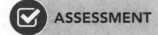 ASSESSMENT

 eTEXT

 APP

Keep an eye out for these **icons**, which indicate the different ways your textbook is enhanced online.

Digital activities are located throughout the narrative to deepen your understanding of scientific concepts.

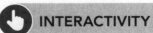 INTERACTIVITY

Interpret models of relationships in various ecosystems.

Elevate your thinking!

California Elevate Science takes science to a whole new level and lets you take ownership of your learning. Explore science in the world around you. Investigate how things work. Think critically and solve problems! *California Elevate Science* helps you think like a scientist, so you're ready for a world of discoveries.

Exploring California

California spotlights explore California phenomena. Topic Quests help connect lesson concepts together and reflect 3-dimensional learning.

- Science concepts organized around phenomena
- Topics weave together 3-D learning
- Engineering focused on solving problems and improving designs

Student Discourse

California Elevate Science promotes active discussion, higher order thinking and analysis and prepares you for high school through:

- High-level write-in prompts
- Evidence-based arguments
- Practice in speaking and writing

California Spotlight
Instructional Segment 2

Before the Topics
Identify the Problem

California Flood Management

Phenomenon In February of 2017, workers at the Orov...

Quest KICKOFF

How can you use solids, liquids, and gases to lift a car?

STEM Phenomenon Auto mechanics often need to go under cars to repair the parts in the under-carriage, such as the shocks and exhaust ...

Model It

Crystalline and Amorphous Solids
Figure 5 A pat of butter is an amorphous solid. The particles that make up the butter are not arranged in a regular pattern. The sapphire gem stones are crystalline solids. Draw what you think the particles look like in a crystalline solid.

READING CHECK Explain In your own words, explain the main differences between crystalline solids and amorphous solids.

Quest CHECK-IN

In this lesson, you learned what happens to the particles of substances during melting, freezing, evaporation, boiling, condensation, and sublimation. You also thought about how thermal energy plays a role in these changes of state.

Predict Why do you need to take the temperature of the surroundings into consideration when designing a system with materials that can change state?

Academic Vocabulary

In orange juice, bits of pulp are suspended in liquid. Explain what you think *suspended* means.

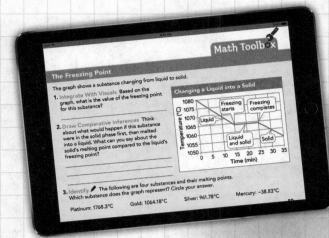

Build Literacy Skills

By connecting science to other disciplines like:

- Mathematics
- Reading and Writing
- STEM/Engineering

Focus on Inquiry

Case studies put you in the shoes of a scientist to solve real-world mysteries using real data. You will be able to:

- Analyze data
- Formulate claims
- Build evidence-based arguments

Enter the Digital Classroom

Virtual labs, 3-D expeditions, and dynamic videos take science beyond the classroom.

- Open-ended virtual labs
- Google Expeditions and field trips
- NBC Learn videos

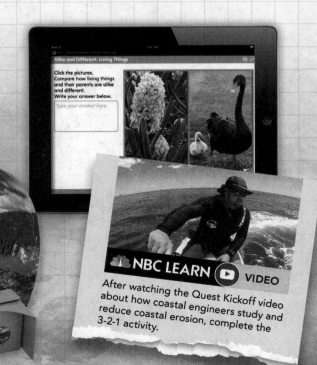

How can digital technologies be used to sustain biodiversity and mitigate the negative impacts of human activities?

Explore It

Look at the picture. What do you observe? What questions do you have about the phenomenon? Write your observations and questions in the space below.

....

....

....

....

....

....

....

....

....

....

....

....

....

....

....

....

....

....

California Spotlight
Instructional Segment 4

MS-PS2-3, MS-PS2-5, MS-PS4-2,
MS-PS4-3, MS-ESS3-4, MS-ETS1-1,
EP&CIIa, EP&CIIc

Inquiry

- What are the characteristic properties and behaviors of waves?
- What human activities harm Earth's biodiversity, and what human activities help sustain local and global biodiversity?
- How does communications technology encode information and how can digital technologies be used to help sustain biodiversity?

Topics

The SMART Way to Track Wildlife

Phenomenon For decades, scientists have used radio-tracking devices to learn about California wildlife from a distance. The device, usually a collar or a tag attached to an animal, sends out radio signals. Scientists track an animal's movements by monitoring these signals. Tracking devices use radio waves to transmit data through the atmosphere.

This California condor, an endangered species, is wearing a lightweight GPS tracker.

Technology for Biodiversity

Scientists are developing new tracking devices that are smaller, lighter, and can be powered for longer periods of time. These new devices will allow scientists to better track and monitor animals in the wild.

As humans develop more land to provide homes and resources for a growing human population, wild animals are losing their natural habitats. Experts need to study not only how animals behave in the wild, but also how and where human activities affect them.

The new tracking devices can collect detailed data about a species. Researchers will be able to learn where the animals go, how they spend their time, and how they use and interact with their habitats. By learning more about animal behavior, conservation managers and wildlife researchers are better prepared to design policies and programs that support wildlife.

A biologist with the California Department of Fish and Game uses a device to locate bighorn sheep wearing trackers in the Sierra Nevada Mountains. Sierra Nevada bighorn sheep are an endangered species in California.

CCC Cause and Effect With a partner, identify and discuss some of the advantages of using radio-tracking devices. Record your ideas below.

....

....

....

....

....

Types of Tracking Devices

The main types of radio-tracking devices used are VHF (Very High Frequency), GPS (Global Positioning System), and satellite tracking. These technologies all depend on electric circuits, electromagnetic waves, electromagnetic signals, computer software, and satellites. In this segment, you will be learning about waves and information technologies, which are important to understand how these devices work.

VHF tracking uses a transmitter, a radio receiver, and an antenna. The transmitter gives off a unique radio signal that allows the animal to be tracked. The receiver must be tuned to the transmitter's frequency to pick up the signal. The antenna is moved back and forth, and the direction of the strongest signal is used to determine the animal's location.

Satellite devices use a much higher-powered transmitter attached to an animal. The transmitter sends an ultra-high frequency (UHF) signal to satellites. The satellites determine the animal's location and send the data to a researcher.

SEP Develop Models 🖋
Consider how an animal's GPS location gets to the researcher's computer. Draw arrows to indicate two paths of data transmission.

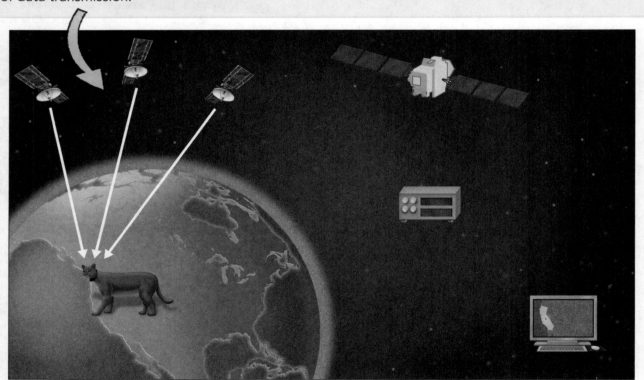

GPS devices use satellites to determine an animal's location over time. A GPS device in the tracking collar receives radio signals transmitted from GPS satellites orbiting Earth. There are three ways to get the data stored in the GPS receiver:

(1) catch the animal and remove the receiver, (2) download the data wirelessly to a portable device that can be transferred to a computer, or (3) relay the data to the Advanced Research and Global Observation Satellite (ARGOS) and then download it to a computer.

SMART Collars

Pumas, or mountain lions, are a keystone species in California. This means pumas influence the survival of many other plant and animal species in an ecosystem. Pumas, therefore, help to maintain the biodiversity in an area. As the human population in California has increased, however, the puma's habitat has become broken up.

To understand the impact of human development on puma behavior in the Santa Cruz Mountains, scientists at the University of California, Santa Cruz, have developed a new high-tech tracking collar. The collar is named the SMART collar, which stands for Species Movement, Acceleration, and Radio Tracking.

The SMART collar has advantages over VHF and GPS tracking technologies. VHF and GPS trackers can identify the location of an animal and the distance it travels. But they cannot track or record more detailed information to provide a more complete picture of an animal's behavior and health. With the wealth of data from the SMART collars, researchers will have a better idea of how to help the remaining puma populations.

This puma in the Santa Cruz Mountains in California is wearing a SMART collar. This device not only tracks the puma's location, but it also gathers data on speed, distance covered, sleep and eating patterns, and other physiological information.

Environmental Interactions

SMART collars are equipped with cameras, accelerometers, magnetometers, and GPS receivers. The accelerometer measures and records the animal's motions in three dimensions. It can record these data up to 32 times per second. By analyzing these data, scientists can determine how fast the animal moves, how high it jumps, how active it is at different times of day or season, and how it attacks its prey. The magnetometer is an electronic compass. It measures the direction in which the animal is moving, based on the orientation of the collar with respect to Earth's magnetic field.

The SMART collar's GPS unit uses radio waves to communicate with satellites and uploads the animal's position at set time intervals. Scientists can combine the sensor's information with other environmental data, such as weather and temperature, to learn more about how an animal interacts with its environment and how it might be affected by climate change.

A female gray wolf has been captured and sedated in order to be fitted with a radio-tracking collar. Scientists hope that the data collected will help them make the best wildlife management decisions.

CCC Stability and Change Suppose you are developing a plan to manage a population of gray wolves. Why is it important to consider actions that maintain stable conditions in the wolves' habitat?

....

....

....

Ask Questions

What questions can you ask to help you make sense of this phenomena?

Waves

Investigative Phenomenon
How can you model the behavior
and properties of waves?

MS-PS4-1 Use mathematical representations to
describe a simple model for waves that includes
how the amplitude of a wave is related to the
energy in a wave.

MS-PS4-2 Develop and use a model to describe
that waves are reflected, absorbed, or transmitted
through various materials.

What does
this device do?

What questions do you have about the phenomenon?

....

....

....

....

....

....

....

....

....

....

① Wave Properties

HANDS-ON LAB

uInvestigate Model the three different types of mechanical waves.

MS-PS4-1 Use mathematical representations to describe a simple model for waves that includes how the amplitude of a wave is related to the energy in a wave.

Connect It !

✏️ **Read the caption, and then label the photos with different types of waves that are indicated in some way by the photos.**

SEP Engage in Argument How is Earth dependent on the sun for energy?

....

....

Connect to Society How is a tsunami warning system a benefit to society?

....

....

Types of Waves

When you think of a wave, you probably picture a surface wave on the ocean. Actually, a **wave** is any disturbance that transfers energy from place to place. An ocean wave is one type of wave called a **mechanical wave**, meaning it moves through some type of matter. The matter a wave travels through is called a **medium**. A mechanical wave cannot travel through a **vacuum**, such as space.

Sound waves are another type of mechanical wave. Sound can travel through the ocean, but it can also travel through a solid object, such as a piece of metal, or a gas, such as the air. It cannot travel through a vacuum such as space.

Another type of wave is an electromagnetic wave. This type of wave transfers electromagnetic radiation, a type of energy. Examples of electromagnetic radiation include visible light, radio waves, X-rays, and microwaves. Like mechanical waves, electromagnetic waves transfer energy. However, electromagnetic waves are unique in that they can travel without a medium.

Both types of waves involve a transfer of energy without a transfer of matter. While mechanical waves travel *through* matter, the waves themselves do not move the matter to a new place.

Figure 1 shows several different types of waves at work. Ocean waves cause the buoy to bob in the water. If a seafloor sensor detects a wave called a *tsunami* (soo NAH mee), it sends a signal to the buoy, which then sends a radio signal to a satellite orbiting Earth. The signal gets relayed to scientists, who can then warn coastal communities. The sunlight that lights this scene is also a kind of wave.

Reflect Write down some examples of waves that you are familiar with from everyday life. Which of these waves can you classify as mechanical waves?

World of Waves
Figure 1 A tsunameter is a buoy anchored to the ocean floor. It detects extremely large waves called tsunamis and sends a radio signal to warn people. In 1964, a tsunami devastated the town of Crescent City, California.

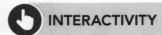

INTERACTIVITY

See how the energy and amplitude of a wave are related.

Transverse Waves Waves can be classified by how energy is transmitted. Energy is transmitted through a medium by mechanical waves. Electromagnetic waves are capable of transmitting energy through empty space.

Waves can also be classified by how the particles in a disturbance vibrate. A mechanical wave begins when a source of energy causes a medium to vibrate. The direction of the vibration determines what type of mechanical wave is produced. A **transverse wave** travels perpendicular (at right angles) to the direction of the source's motion. The person in **Figure 2** is using his arms to make up-and-down vibrations in two ropes. Each particle of the rope moves up and down. The direction the waves travel, though, is perpendicular to that up-and-down motion. The energy is transmitted toward the far ends of the ropes.

The curved shape of the rope shows the main features of a transverse wave. The high point of a wave is its crest, and the low point is the trough. Halfway between the crest and trough is the wave's resting position. The distance between the highest part of the crest and the resting position marks the wave's **amplitude**. In general, the amplitude of a wave is the maximum distance the medium vibrates from the rest position.

Electromagnetic waves, such as sunlight, are also transverse waves. In their case, however, there is no motion of particles, even when light travels through a liquid, such as water, or a solid, such as glass.

Transverse Waves

Figure 2 ✏ Use arrows to indicate the direction the rope is vibrating and the direction energy is flowing. Label a crest and a trough, and indicate the amplitude.

Longitudinal Waves

A wave that travels in the same direction as the vibrations that produce it is called a **longitudinal wave**. Sound is a longitudinal wave. Sound travels from speakers when flat surfaces inside the speakers vibrate in and out, compressing and expanding the air next to them.

Figure 3 shows a longitudinal wave in a spring toy. When the left hand pulls on the toy, the result is a series of stretches and compressions. Gaps between compressions are called *rarefactions*. Energy moves to the right along the toy.

While the wave travels, the spring particles do not move all the way to the right, as the wave does. Each spring particle moves back and forth, like the hand. The small piece of ribbon on the spring shows how the particles in the spring move.

Literacy Connection

Integrate Information As you learn about waves, take notes that summarize and categorize the different motions that waves produce.

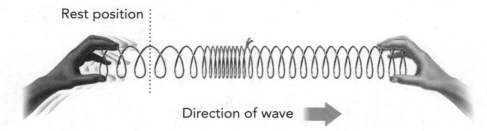

Rest position

Direction of wave

Longitudinal Wave
Figure 3 🖊 Label a compression and a rarefaction.

Surface Waves

Combinations of transverse and longitudinal waves are called *surface waves*. For example, an ocean wave travels at the surface of water. When a wave passes through water, the water (and anything on it) vibrates up and down. The water also moves back and forth slightly in the direction that the wave is traveling. The up-and-down and back-and-forth movements combine to make each particle of water move in a circle, as shown in **Figure 4**.

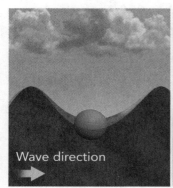

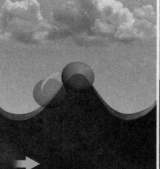

Wave direction

Ball's motion

Surface Wave
Figure 4 As waves move from left to right, they cause the ball to move in a circle.

✅ CHECK POINT **Compare and Contrast** What is the main difference between a surface wave and a longitudinal wave?

....

....

Properties of Waves

Figure 5 All waves have amplitude, wavelength, frequency, and speed. After you read about these properties, answer the questions above the diagrams.

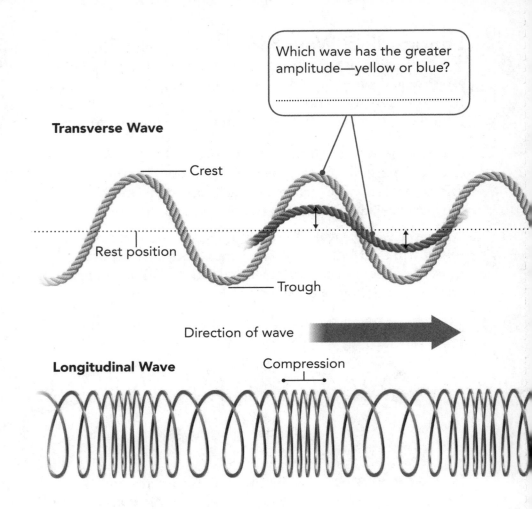

Which wave has the greater amplitude—yellow or blue?

....

Transverse Wave

Crest

Rest position

Trough

Direction of wave

Longitudinal Wave

Compression

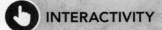
Properties of Waves

In addition to amplitude, all waves have three other properties: wavelength, frequency, and speed. These properties are all related to one another.

Wavelength You have seen that a wave repeats as it travels. Its **wavelength** is determined by the distance it travels before it starts to repeat. The wavelength of a transverse wave is the distance from crest to crest, as shown in **Figure 5**. For a longitudinal wave, the wavelength is the distance from one compression to the next.

Frequency The number of times a wave repeats in a given amount of time is called its **frequency**. You can also think of frequency as the number of waves that pass a given point in a certain amount of time. For example, if you make waves on a rope so that one wave passes by a point every second, the frequency is 1 wave per second. Frequency is measured in units called hertz (Hz). A wave that occurs every second has a frequency of 1 Hz. If two waves pass by in a second, the frequency is 2 Hz.

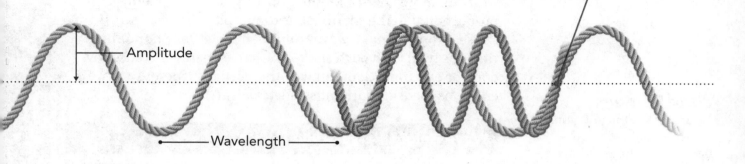

One yellow wave passes by this point each second, so the frequency of the yellow wave is ....

Two green waves pass by this point each second, so the frequency of the green wave is ....

Amplitude

Wavelength

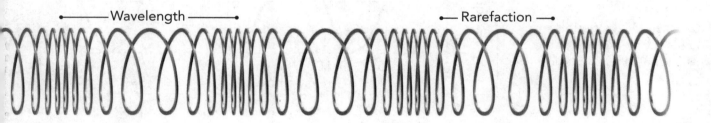

Wavelength

Rarefaction

Speed The speed of a wave is the distance it travels in a unit of time. Different waves have different speeds. For instance, a light wave travels almost a million times faster than a sound wave travels through air! Waves also travel at different speeds through different materials. For example, light travels faster through water than through glass. Sound travels more than three times faster through water than through air.

To calculate a wave's speed, divide the distance it travels by the time it takes to travel that distance. You can also find a wave's speed if you know its wavelength and frequency—just multiply wavelength times frequency.

Wave speed = Wavelength × Frequency

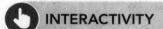

INTERACTIVITY

Generate virtual waves in a wave pool.

☑ CHECK POINT **Predict** Suppose you and a friend are standing at opposite ends of a gymnasium and one of you claps. Will the other person hear the clap at the same time she sees it happen? Explain why or why not.

....

....

VIDEO

See what happens when balls of different masses are dropped in water.

Wave Energy

Waves transmit energy from place to place. The amount of energy they transmit depends on how much energy was input by the original source of the vibration. Faster vibrations transmit more energy. Larger amplitude vibrations also transmit more energy. Mathematically, a wave's energy is proportional to the square of its amplitude. For instance, if you shake a rope to make waves and then move your hand three times as high with each shake, the wave energy increases by a factor of 3 times 3, or 9! Like other forms of energy, a wave's energy is measured in units called *joules* (J).

Wave Motion

Figure 6 In **Figure 5** you saw several waves at the same time. The graph here shows you an interval of time and how the wave height changes as several waves pass a single point.

Integrate With Visuals What is the frequency of the wave? What is its amplitude?

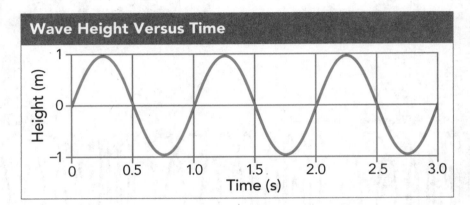

Wave Height Versus Time

Math Toolbox

Wave Properties

🖉 The table shows the properties of waves near the beach on one summer day. Use the relationship between speed, wavelength, and frequency to complete the table. Then answer the questions.

Waves at a Beach				
Time	Amplitude	Wavelength	Frequency	Speed
10 AM	0.4 m	10 m	0.2 Hz	
2 PM	0.2 m		0.1 Hz	2 m/s
6 PM	0.3 m	20 m		3 m/s

1. Use Ratio Reasoning What is the ratio of the amplitude of the 10 AM to the amplitude of the 2 PM wave?

2. Use Proportional Relationships If the amplitude of the 6 PM wave increased to 0.6 m, how many times greater would the energy become?

☑ LESSON 1 Check

MS-PS4-1

1. Explain How can you measure the wavelength of a longitudinal wave?

....

....

....

....

....

....

....

....

2. SEP Use Mathematics A sound wave's frequency is 4 Hz and its wavelength is 8 m. What is the wave's speed?

....

....

....

....

....

....

3. SEP Use Models ✏ Draw a model of a transverse wave. Use lines and labels to show the amplitude and wavelength of the wave.

4. Use Proportional Relationships During a rising tide, ocean waves often become larger. If the amplitude of a wave increases by a factor of 1.1, by how much does the energy increase?

....

....

....

....

....

....

....

5. CCC Cause and Effect If a musician increases the wavelength of the sound waves she produces without changing their speed, what must be happening to the frequency? Explain your answer.

....

....

....

....

....

....

....

....

....

....

....

....

LESSON
(2) Wave Interactions

HANDS-ON LAB

uInvestigate See what type of interference you get when you send waves down a coil.

MS-PS4-2 Develop and use a model to describe that waves are reflected, absorbed, or transmitted through various materials.

Connect It!

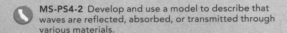

🖉 **Look at the image of the rocks reflected in the lake. Draw a line where you think the surface of the water is.**

SEP Construct Explanations Why are the rocks reflected so clearly on the water?

....

....

....

....

Reflection, Refraction, and Absorption

If you've ever been to the beach, you've seen how different kinds of waves move. Some ocean waves crash into rocks or piers, while others reach the shore smoothly. Rays of sunlight hit the surface of the water, and some bounce off while others pass through. In general, when waves encounter different media, they are either reflected, transmitted, or absorbed.

Reflection Some waves are completely blocked by an obstruction, but their energy is not absorbed or converted to another form of energy. These types of waves bounce off, or reflect from, those obstructions. In a **reflection**, the wave bounces off and heads in a different direction. The law of reflection states that the angle of incidence equals the angle of reflection. This means that the angle at which the wave strikes the material will match the angle at which the reflected wave bounces off that material, as shown in **Figure 2**. Light reflecting from a mirror is the most familiar example of reflection. The echo of your voice from the walls of a canyon is another example.

Reflection

Figure 2 A flashlight beam reflects off of a mirror at the same angle it strikes.

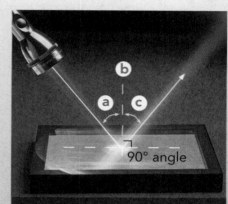

a Angle of incidence The angle between the incoming wave and the normal.

b Normal A line perpendicular to the surface at the point where reflection occurs.

c Angle of reflection The angle between the reflected wave and the normal.

Tufa Reflections

Figure 1 Light waves reflecting off the surface of the water of Mono Lake in California creates a mirror image of these rock formations known as tufa towers.

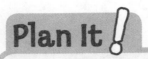

Plan It

SEP Develop Models ✏️ Have you ever seen a movie scene in which a character appears to be looking at a mirror, yet the camera is not visible in the mirror? Think about how the director sets up this scene. Draw a setup that shows the position of the actor, the camera, and the mirror, and demonstrate why the camera's image is not visible to the camera.

Refraction

Figure 3 Light rays bend as they enter water because one side of the wave fronts slows down in water while the other side continues at the same speed in air.

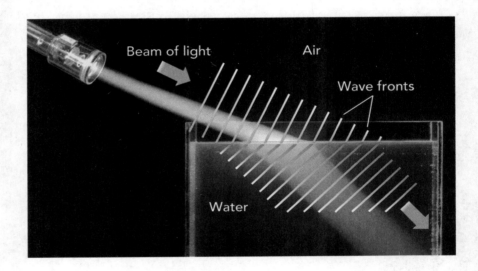

Academic Vocabulary

What is another way for saying that a wave is "transmitted" through a medium?

....

....

....

Refraction Imagine riding a bike down a smooth asphalt road. When you turn off the road onto a dirt path, the transition can be jarring. You might have to grip the handlebars hard to keep the bike going straight as the two wheels are on different surfaces.

When light waves are **transmitted** from one medium into another, they also bend in different directions. This bending is due to **refraction**, or the bending of waves due to a change in speed.

When a wave enters a new medium at an angle other than perpendicular, it changes direction. For instance, when light is directed at water at an angle, as in **Figure 3**, the light slows down and bends downward. The wave front bends toward the normal, the imaginary line that runs perpendicular to the boundary between the two media.

Diffraction Did you ever wonder how you can hear someone speaking even around the corner of a building or doorway? This is an example of **diffraction**. Waves don't only travel in straight lines. They also bend around objects.

You can observe diffraction with water waves as well as sound waves. Water waves can diffract around a rock or an island in the ocean. Because tsunami waves can diffract all the way around an island, people on the shores of the entire island are at risk.

Absorption When you think of something being absorbed, you might think of how a paper towel soaks up water. Waves can be absorbed by certain materials, too. In **absorption**, the energy of a wave is transferred to the material it encounters. When ocean waves reach a shoreline, most of their energy is absorbed by the shore.

When light waves encounter the surface of a different medium or material, the light waves may be reflected, refracted, or absorbed. What happens to the waves depends on the type of material they hit. Light is mostly absorbed by dark materials, such as the surface of a parking lot, and mostly reflected by light materials, such as snow.

Literacy Connection

Integrate Information
As you read, classify the phenomena you learn about as either interactions between waves and media or interactions among waves.

Reflect What are some ways in which you use reflection in your everyday life? Are there things you have to keep in mind when you use reflective devices, such as mirrors?

VIDEO
Discover how reflection and absorption create echoes.

Question It!

Classify ✏ Identify each picture as being an example of reflection, refraction, or absorption.

uInvestigate See what type of interference you get when you send waves down a coil.

Wave Interference

Have you ever seen two ocean waves from opposite directions meet so they momentarily form a bigger, hill-like shape before continuing in their original directions? This is an example of wave **interference**. There are two types.

Constructive Interference
The example of two waves of similar sizes meeting and forming a wave with an amplitude greater than either of the original waves is called *constructive interference*. You can think of it as waves "helping each other," or adding their energies together. As shown in **Figure 4**, when the crests of two waves overlap, they make a higher crest. If two troughs overlap, they make a deeper trough. In both cases, the amplitude of the combined crests or troughs increases.

Types of Interference

Figure 4 ✏ Write captions to describe three parts of destructive interference. Complete the key to explain what the different arrows mean in the images.

Constructive Interference

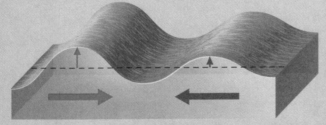

1 Two waves approach each other. The wave on the left has a greater amplitude.

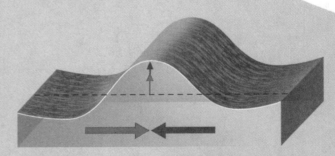

2 The new crest's amplitude is the sum of the amplitudes of the original crests.

Destructive Interference

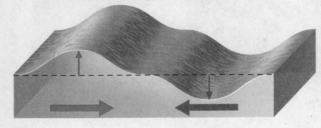

1 ....
....

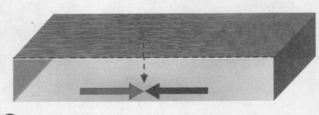

2 ....
....

Destructive Interference

When two waves combine to form a wave with a smaller amplitude than either original wave had, the effect is called *destructive interference*. Destructive interference occurs when the crest of one wave overlaps the trough of another wave. If the crest has a larger amplitude than the trough of the other wave, the crest "wins," and part of it remains. If the original trough has a larger amplitude than the crest of the other wave, the result is a trough. If a crest and trough have equal amplitudes, they cancel each other out, as shown in **Figure 4**. Destructive interference is used in noise-canceling headphones to block out distracting noises in a listener's surroundings.

✓ CHECK POINT **Infer** Which type of wave interference could cause sound to become louder? Explain your answer.

....

....

....

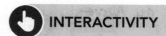
INTERACTIVITY

Observe wave interference in a rope and in surface waves.

Interfering Waves

Figure 5 Ripples created by rain water on a pond interfere with one another in a pattern that exhibits both constructive and destructive interference.

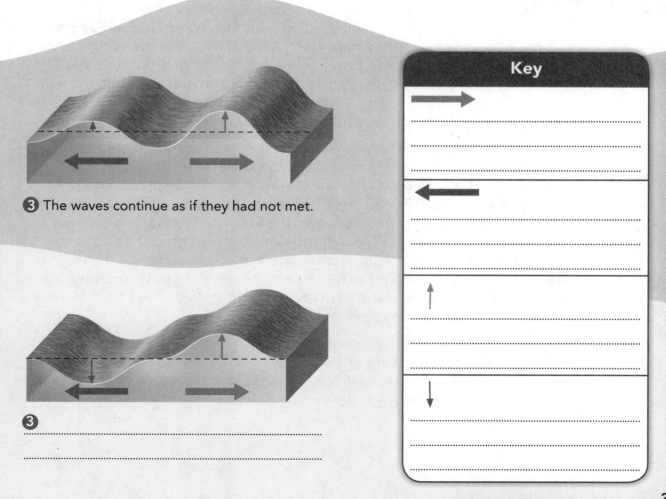

③ The waves continue as if they had not met.

③ ....

....

Key

....

....

....

....

....

....

↑

....

....

....

↓

....

....

....

23

Standing Waves

Figure 6 ✏ As the hand shown at left increases the frequency, the number of wavelengths in the standing wave will increase. In a standing wave, it looks as if there's a mirror image of both the crest and trough. Label the rest of the nodes and antinodes.

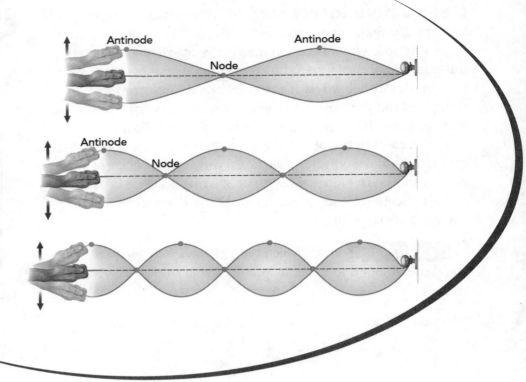

INTERACTIVITY

Describe how waves behave when they interact with a barrier or boundary.

Standing Waves

Look at the rope setup in **Figure 6.** The rope is tied to a doorknob, and someone shakes the free end. This motion generates standing waves. A **standing wave** is a wave that appears to stand in one place. Standing waves are produced by two waves interfering with each other as they travel in opposite directions. Standing waves on the rope appear when an incoming wave and a wave reflected from the doorknob have just the right frequency to interfere as shown.

In a standing wave, destructive interference between the two colliding waves produces points with zero amplitude, called *nodes*. The nodes are always evenly spaced along the wave. Points of maximum amplitude on a standing wave are called antinodes. Antinodes always occur halfway between two nodes. The frequency and wavelength of the interfering waves determine how many nodes and antinodes the standing wave will have. When you see a standing wave, the antinodes appear to wobble in and out from the rope's rest position while the nodes appear motionless.

You may have seen a standing wave in a wash basin or a bowl of soup. A small disturbance starts the water vibrating. The water appears to have a node in the center of the bowl, and the water wave jiggles around that node.

Resonance Think about the last time you swung on a swing at a playground. You may have noticed that it is difficult to get yourself going. Once you are in motion, you can pull on the chains of the swing and pump your legs at the right time to keep yourself swinging. The swing has a natural frequency, and your actions match that frequency to create greater amplitudes in your motion.

Most objects have at least one natural frequency of vibration. Standing waves occur in an object when it vibrates at one of these natural frequencies. If a nearby object vibrates at the same frequency, it can cause resonance. **Resonance** is an increase in the amplitude of a vibration that occurs when external vibrations match an object's natural frequency.

When soldiers march across a bridge, they make sure to stay out of step. If they did not, their footsteps could cause the bridge to swing wildly like the rope in **Figure 6** and collapse.

Understanding the resonance of different materials is also useful for people who build guitars, violins, or other wooden string instruments. If the wood in a guitar, such as the one in **Figure 7**, resonates too much with a certain note, it may sound too loud when that particular note is struck. Likewise, if the wood does not resonate with any particular note, the instrument may sound dull.

☑CHECK POINT **Summarize** In general, why is it risky to build something with a natural frequency that can be matched by external vibrations?

....

....

....

Make Meaning Make a two-column table in your notebook. Use it to record descriptions of constructive interference, destructive interference, standing waves, and resonance.

Musical Resonance
Figure 7 The types of wood and construction techniques used to make a guitar affect aspects of its sound, including its resonance.

MS-PS4-2

1. CCC Cause and Effect Explain what happens to light when it is refracted at the surface of water.

....

....

....

....

....

....

....

....

....

....

3. Explain What does it mean for waves to be absorbed by a certain medium? Make sure to include energy in your explanation.

....

....

....

....

....

....

....

....

....

....

2. SEP Interpret Data The diagrams below show blue wave and a green wave interfering to form a dark blue result. Which of the diagrams depicts constructive interference? Explain your choice using the term *amplitude*.

A.　　　　　B.

....

....

....

....

....

....

....

....

....

....

4. SEP Construct Explanations Why does the transition of light waves from water to air make it seem as if fish and other things in a pond are in shallower water than they actually are?

....

....

....

....

....

....

....

....

....

....

....

....

....

....

....

MS-PS4-2

Say "CHEESE!"

 VIDEO

Find out how cameras work.

For hundreds of years, people used paper and pencils to record what they saw. This all changed in the 1800s with the invention of photography.

The Challenge To continue to improve the ways in which people can record images

Phenomenon Early cameras were large and clumsy objects that formed images on glass or metal. In the 1900s, engineers experimented with smaller and lighter cameras that used film. Today people use digital cameras. But they all use the same process to create images.

Today, cameras used by professionals still have three main parts for capturing light:

- The **lens** is the camera's eye. It collects the light reflected off of what you want to photograph.

- The **aperture** lets light in through the lens. The wider the aperture, the more light is let in.

- The **shutter** is like a curtain that opens when you take the photo.

In a film camera, the light changes the film both physically and chemically to create an image. In a *digital* camera, the light reaches photosensors, which convert the image to a string of numbers.

Cameras have changed tremendously over the years!

 **DESIGN CHALLENGE** Can you build your own simple camera using just a box? Go to the Engineering Design Notebook to find out!

27

(3) Sound Waves

HANDS-ON LAB

 Investigate Use models to examine how sound waves travel through different media.

🕐 **MS-PS4-2** Develop and use a model to describe that waves are reflected, absorbed, or transmitted through various materials.

Connect It !

✏️ **When someone strikes a cymbal, the cymbal vibrates to produce sound. Draw compressions and rarefactions of the air particles as the sound waves travel away from the cymbal.**

SEP Engage in Argument What evidence supports the claim that sound is a mechanical wave?

....

CCC Cause and Effect What do you think happens to a sound wave when the volume of sound increases?

....

The Behavior of Sound

All sound waves begin with a vibration. Look at the woman in **Figure 1.** When she hits a drum or a cymbal with her drumstick, the drum or cymbal vibrates rapidly, disturbing the air particles around the drum set. When the drum or cymbal moves away from its rest position, it creates a compression by pushing air particles together. When it moves back toward its rest position, it creates a rarefaction by causing air particles to spread out.

Recall that sound waves are mechanical waves that require a medium through which to travel. In the case of the drummer and the drum set, the compressions and rarefactions that are created travel through the air. Sound waves, however, travel more easily through liquids and solids. When you set a glass down on a table, for example, the sound waves that are generated travel first through the glass and the table and then are released into the air.

Sound waves are also longitudinal—they travel in the same direction as the vibrations that produce them. Like other types of mechanical waves, sound waves can be reflected, transmitted, absorbed, and diffracted.

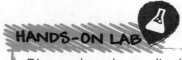
Making Waves
Figure 1 The vibrations caused by hitting drums and cymbals generate sound waves.

INTERACTIVITY

Observe and analyze sound waves in a variety of everyday situations.

Reflection and Transmission

Like other mechanical waves, sound waves that pass through a surface are called *transmitted waves*, and sound waves that bounce off a surface are called *reflected waves*. When a sound wave travels through the air and comes into contact with a solid surface, such as a wall, a portion of the wave passes through the surface. Most of the wave, however, is reflected away from the surface.

Absorption

Have you ever been to a concert in a large indoor theater? If so, you may have noticed panels on the walls. Most large theaters have acoustic panels to help with sound absorption. Sound absorption describes the process of sound waves striking a surface and quickly losing energy. The energy is converted to thermal energy in the surface. Acoustic panels in theaters are porous, meaning they are full of small holes, and they absorb a portion of the sound waves. In the case of a theater, absorption of sound waves improves the listening experience for people at the concert. More sound energy is absorbed than reflected, so the audience does not experience as much interference from reflected sound waves. See **Figure 2** for another example of absorption. Any material with a porous surface can act as a sound absorber.

A Quiet, Snowy Night
Figure 2 Walking along the Merced River in Yosemite National Park, you may observe it is generally quieter when there's snow on the ground than when there's not. Why do you think this is?

....

....

....

Model It

If you've ever shouted into a canyon or a courtyard, then you may have heard an echo. An echo occurs when sound waves are reflected off a hard surface, such as the wall of a rocky mountain. The sound you hear is delayed because it takes time for the sound waves to reflect off the surface and reach your ears.

SEP Develop Models ✏️ Draw a picture of sound waves that produce an echo. In addition to reflected waves, your model should also indicate waves that are transmitted or absorbed.

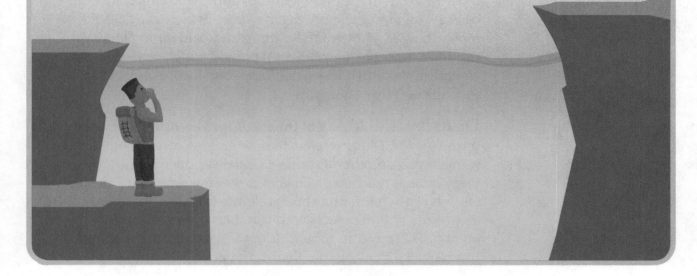

Diffraction It is usually easy to hear someone talking if they are in the same room as you, but you can also hear people in other rooms nearby. Why is this? You can hear them because sound waves can bend around the edges of an opening, such as a doorway. This is called sound diffraction. Sound waves, like water waves, spread out after passing through an opening.

How much sound waves are transmitted, reflected, absorbed, or diffracted depends greatly upon the medium through which they travel. If sound waves travel through air and hit a solid surface, such as a concrete wall, much of the energy in the waves is reflected back toward the source. If the surfaces they hit are softer or more porous, then more energy will be absorbed. Sound waves will be diffracted around corners and through passageways between hard surfaces.

HANDS-ON LAB

Investigate Use models to examine how sound waves travel through different media.

☑ **CHECK POINT** **Summarize** What are four things that can happen to sound waves when they reach a barrier?

....

....

▶ VIDEO

Explore what thunder is and how to determine your distance from an approaching storm.

Speed of Sound

Figure 3 ✏ Rate the speed of sound through the medium in each container, with 1 being the fastest and 3 being the slowest.

Factors Affecting the Speed of Sound

As you have read, sound waves are mechanical waves that require a medium through which to travel. The characteristics of the medium have an effect on the speed of the sound waves traveling through them. The main factors that affect the speed of sound are compressibility, stiffness, density, and temperature.

Stiffness In general, sound waves travel faster in materials that are stiffer, meaning harder to compress. This is because of how efficiently the movement of one particle will move another. Think of the coins, water, and air in **Figure 3**. Solids are less compressible than liquids, which are less compressible than gases. Therefore, sound waves travel fastest in solids and slowest in gases.

Density The density of the medium also affects the speed of sound waves. Density refers to how much matter or mass there is in a given amount of space. The denser the material, the more mass it has in a given volume, so the greater its inertia. Objects with greater inertia accelerate less from an energy disturbance than objects with less inertia, or less massive objects. Therefore, in materials of the same stiffness, sound travels more slowly in the denser material.

Temperature The temperature of a medium also affects the speed at which sound waves travel through it, though in more complicated ways. For solids, an increase in temperature reduces the stiffness, so the sound speed decreases. For fluids, such as air, the increase in temperature reduces the density, so the sound speed generally increases.

☑ CHECK POINT **Hypothesize** Would sound waves travel more slowly through air at the North Pole or at the equator? Explain.

....

....

....

....

Loudness and Pitch

How might you describe a sound? You might call it loud or soft, high or low. When you turn up the volume of your speakers, you increase the loudness of a sound. When you sing higher and higher notes, you increase the pitch of your voice. Loudness and pitch depend on different properties of sound waves.

Factors Affecting Loudness You use the term **loudness** to describe your awareness of the energy of a sound. How loud a sound is depends on the energy and intensity of the sound waves. If someone knocks lightly on your front door, then you might hear a quiet sound. If they pound on your door, then you hear a much louder sound. Why is that so? The pounding transfers much more energy through the door than a light knock does. That's because a hard knock on a door produces a much greater amplitude in the sound waves than a softer knock does. Increased energy results in greater intensity of the waves. **Intensity** is the amount of energy a sound wave carries per second through a unit area. The closer the sound wave is to its source, the more energy it has in a given area. As the sound wave moves away from the source, the wave spreads out and the intensity decreases.

INTERACTIVITY

Explore how the frequency and intensity of a sound wave affect the sound you hear through headphones.

Intensity of Sound

Figure 4 ✏ Sound waves spread out as they travel away from the source producing the sound. For each of the locations in the image, rank the intensity of the sound waves coming from the band on a scale of 1 to 3, with 1 being the greatest intensity.

Academic Vocabulary

What is the root word in *differentiate*? How does this help you figure out the word's meaning?

....

....

....

....

....

....

Measuring Loudness

So, how do our ears **differentiate** between a light knock and a hard knock on a door? Loudness can be measured with a unit called a **decibel** (dB). The greater the number of decibels of the sound, the louder that sound seems to a listener. The loudness of a sound you can barely hear, such as a pin dropping to the floor, is about 0 dB. When someone lightly taps on your door, the loudness is about 30 dB. But if someone pounds on your door, that loudness might increase to 80 dB! Sounds louder than 100 dB, such as the sound of a chainsaw, can cause damage to people's ears, especially if they are exposed to the sounds for long periods of time. Music technicians use equalizers to change the loudness levels of different frequencies of sound, as in **Figure 5**.

Using an Equalizer

Figure 5 You can use an equalizer to adjust the loudness of sound waves at different frequencies. Raising the decibel level of low frequencies increases the bass tones of music. How might you increase the high-pitched tones of music?

....

....

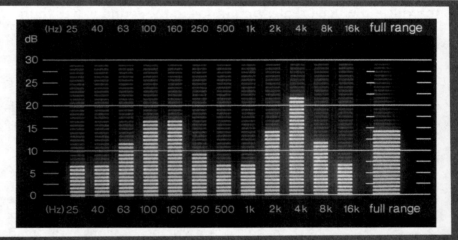

Math Toolbox

Decibel Levels

Every 10-decibel increase represents a tenfold increase in intensity and power. For example, when loudness increases from 20 to 30 decibels, a sound's power is multiplied by 10. If loudness increases by 10 again, power increases by another factor of 10. Therefore, when loudness increases from 20 to 40 decibels, power increases by a factor of 100!

1. **Use Ratio Reasoning** If a sound's power level increases from 20 decibels to 50 decibels, by what factor does its power increase?

....

....

2. **Reason Quantitatively** If you want to lower the loudness of the bass tones in your music by 20 decibels, by how much does the intensity need to decrease?

....

Thickness Affects Pitch
Figure 6 On this six-string guitar, the strings range in thickness.
✎ On the photo, draw an X on the guitar string that has the lowest pitch.

Factors Affecting Pitch Have you ever heard someone describe a note on a piano as "high-pitched" or "low-pitched"? The **pitch** of a sound refers to how high or low the sound seems. Pitch depends upon the frequency of the sound waves. Sound waves with a high frequency have a high pitch, and waves with a low frequency have a low pitch.

The frequency of a sound wave depends upon how fast the source of the sound is vibrating. For example, when people speak or sing, the air from their lungs moves past their vocal cords and makes the cords vibrate, producing sound waves. When vocal cords vibrate more quickly, they produce higher-frequency sound waves with higher pitches. When vocal cords vibrate more slowly, they produce lower-frequency sound waves with lower pitches.

This phenomenon happens with all things that vibrate and produce sound waves. Guitars produce sound when someone strums or plucks their strings. If you've ever studied a guitar, then you may have noticed that its strings vary in thickness. The thicker strings of a guitar vibrate more slowly than the thinner strings do, and so the thicker strings have a lower frequency, and therefore a lower pitch, than the thinner strings (**Figure 6**).

INTERACTIVITY

Explain how sounds from moving objects can change in pitch.

Literacy Connection

Integrate with Visuals
Do you think the motorcyclist would hear a change in pitch of the motorcycle's sound as he passes by you? Explain why or why not.

....

....

....

....

....

The Doppler Effect

Have you ever had a loud motorcycle drive by you and heard the pitch of the engine noise change? Change in pitch occurs because the movement of the source of the sound causes a sound wave to either compress or stretch. As the motorcycle approaches, the peaks of the emitted sound waves are squeezed together. When the peaks are closer together, the sound waves have a higher frequency. As the motorcycle moves away, the peaks of the emitted sound waves are spread out. The sound waves then have a lower frequency.

A change in frequency is perceived by a listener as a change in pitch. This change in frequency (and therefore, in pitch) of the sound wave in relation to an observer is called the **Doppler effect. Figure 7** shows the Doppler effect when a firetruck speeds by a person on the sidewalk.

✓ CHECK POINT **Summarize** What property of a sound wave determines the pitch of a sound?

....

The Doppler Effect

Figure 7 As a firetruck speeds by, an observer detects changes in the pitch of the truck's siren. The firetruck approaches the observer in the first image. It then passes her and continues on.

CCC Cause and Effect
✏ Draw the sound waves as the truck moves away.

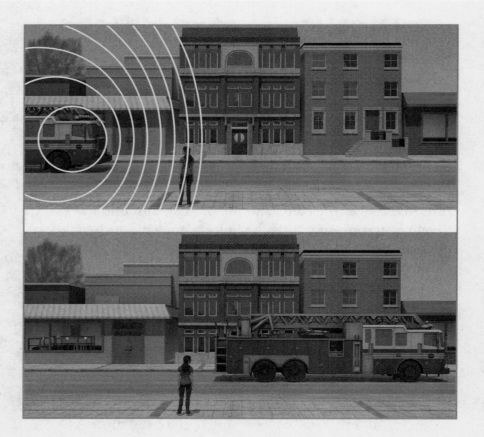

MS-PS4-2

1. Identify What is the cause of any sound wave?

....

2. SEP Communicate Information Why does sound travel more quickly through a solid than through a liquid or a gas?

....

....

....

....

....

....

3. Form a Hypothesis Dogs can hear higher-pitched sounds than humans can. How do you think the sound frequencies that dogs can hear compare to the frequencies that humans can hear?

....

....

....

....

....

4. CCC Cause and Effect What effect might spending years working on a construction site have on a person's hearing? Explain.

....

....

....

....

....

....

....

5. Apply Concepts Ultrasound, also known as sonography, is a technology that uses high-frequency sound waves to produce images. It is used to help doctors see inside patients' bodies. How do you think the sound waves can be used to show bones, muscles, and other internal structures?

....

....

....

....

....

....

....

....

6. SEP Develop Models Imagine a person is sitting on a beach, and a speedboat passes by on the water. Draw a model of this situation, and indicate how the Doppler effect would influence how the sound waves coming from the boat would be perceived by the person on shore.

4 Light

uInvestigate Discover how light is reflected, refracted, and transmitted.

MS-PS4-2 Develop and use a model to describe that waves are reflected, absorbed, or transmitted through various materials.

Connect It!

✏️ **Shadows are made by different objects in the picture. Label two shadows with the names of the objects that made them.**

SEP Construct Explanations Why do some objects make shadows, while others do not?

....

....

....

....

....

Light, Color, and Objects

When people talk about light, they are usually referring to the part of the electromagnetic spectrum that is visible to humans. This light interacts with the world around us to determine what we see and how it appears. In the wave model of light, brightness depends on the amplitude of the electromagnetic waves.

Materials can be classified based on how much light passes through them. A material that transmits most of the light that strikes it is **transparent**. You can see through a transparent object, such as a window pane or the plastic wrap on a package.

A **translucent** material scatters the light that passes through it. You might be able to see through a translucent material, but the image will look blurred. Waxed paper and gelatin dessert are examples of translucent materials.

A material that reflects or absorbs all of the light that strikes it is called **opaque**. A book, a marshmallow, and a hippopotamus are all opaque—you can't see through them because light does not pass through them. **Figure 1** shows an example of what happens when light strikes transparent and opaque objects.

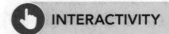
INTERACTIVITY

Write about the appearance of your own reflection on several materials.

Reflect Explain why you have a shadow, but a window pane does not.

Shadows
Figure 1 You can see shadows of both the person and the window frame. There is no shadow of the panes of glass in the window, because light passes through them.

39

INTERACTIVITY

Observe and describe the behavior of light in various situations.

The Color of Objects

Recall that white light is a mixture of all of the colors in the rainbow. In the wave model of light, each color has a different frequency. When white light shines on a white object, all the colors of light are reflected. For colored objects, some of the colors are reflected, and some are absorbed.

The color of an opaque object is the color of light that the object reflects. It absorbs all other colors. Under white light, the soccer ball in **Figure 2** appears blue and red. It reflects blue and red wavelengths of light and absorbs all other colors. At the bottom you can see how the ball looks in different colors of light. In blue light, the blue hexagons reflect, so they appear blue. The red pentagons absorb blue light, so they look black. In red light, the hexagons reflect, and in green light there is no reflection. The ball absorbs all the light, so it looks black.

The color of a transparent or a translucent object is the color of light that passes through it. For example, the color of a clear, green drinking glass is green because green light is the only color of light that passes through it.

CHECK POINT **Determine Central Ideas** Why does snow appear white?

Light and Color

Figure 2 When light shines on an object, some wavelengths of light are reflected and some are absorbed. ✎ Circle the answers that correctly complete the sentences. The color of an opaque object is the color of light it (absorbs / reflects). If the object (absorbs / reflects) all of the light, the object appears black.

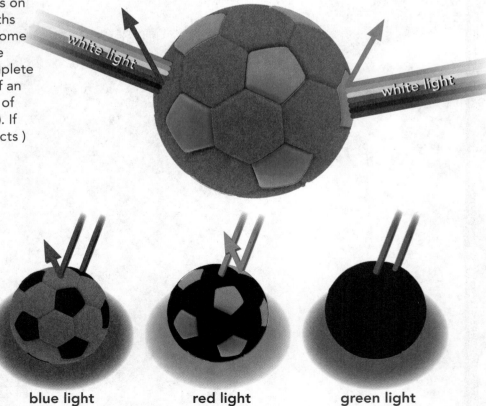

blue light   red light   green light

Color Filters

Perhaps you have looked at an object that has a colored light shining on it. You might have noticed that the color of the object looks different than it does when white light shines on it. The color of the light might come from white light shining through a colored filter—a tinted piece of glass or plastic. A red filter, for example, transmits only red light. When light shines through a red filter onto an object, any part of the object that is red, looks red. Any other color looks black. **Figure 3** shows several different color filters and what happens when white light shines on them.

Color filters are often used in photography and movies. They are part of the special effects that create different moods for scenes. Use what you know about filters to complete the activity in **Figure 3**.

INTERACTIVITY

Explore how color filters affect the appearance of different objects.

Literacy Connection

Evaluate Media Describe an image you've seen with a filter on it, and write about how the filter altered the image.

....

....

....

....

Photography and Color Filters

Figure 3 🖊 Color filters can be used on this image of the Golden Gate Bridge to bring out certain colors or create dramatic moods. For each of the inset images, write the color of the filter that produced the altered images.

41

Reflecting Light

You have seen that sometimes light is transmitted through materials. Like other electromagnetic radiation, light can also be reflected. The reflection of light occurs when rays of light bounce off a surface. Reflected light produces your image in a mirror, but reflected light also produces a distorted image or no image at all in the surface of rippling water on a lake. The difference lies in whether the light undergoes regular reflection or diffuse reflection.

Regular reflection occurs when parallel rays of light hit a smooth surface. As shown in **Figure 4**, the trees are reflected because light hits the smooth surface of the water, and the rays all reflect at the same angle. As a result, the reflection is a clear image.

In **diffuse reflection**, parallel rays of light hit an uneven surface. The angle at which each ray hits the surface equals the angle at which it reflects. The rays, however, don't bounce off in the same direction because the light rays hit different parts of the surface at different angles. **Figure 4** shows why light undergoes diffuse reflection when it hits choppy water on a lake.

Regular and Diffuse Reflection

Figure 4 Light reflects off the surface of water.
 For each type of reflection, circle the terms that correctly complete the sentence.

You (can / cannot) see an image in the still water because the light undergoes (regular / diffuse) reflection.

You (can / cannot) see an image in the choppy water because the light undergoes (regular / diffuse) reflection.

Mirror Images

The most common way to form a clear image using reflected light is with a mirror. There are three different types of mirrors—plane, convex, and concave. The types of mirrors are distinguished by the shape of the surface of the mirror.

The mirror you have hanging on a wall in your home probably is a flat mirror, also known as a *plane mirror*. The image you see in the mirror is called a virtual image, which is an image that forms where light seems to come from. **Figure 5** shows an example of a virtual image in a plane mirror. This image is upright and the same size as the object that formed the image, but the right and left sides of the image are reversed.

Convex Mirrors

To visualize a convex mirror, think about a metal bowl. A **convex** mirror is like the outside of the bowl because it is a mirror with a surface that curves outward. If you look at an image in the outside of the bowl, it is smaller than the image in a plane mirror. **Figure 6** shows an example of an image in a convex mirror. To understand how these images form, look at the optical axis and the focal point of the mirror. The optical axis is an imaginary line that divides a mirror in half. The **focal point** is the location at which rays parallel to the optical axis reflect and meet. The light reflects off the curved surface such that the image appears to come from a focal point behind the mirror.

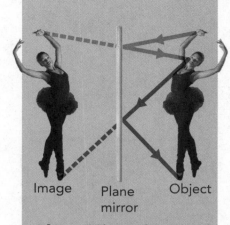

Image   Plane   Object
mirror

Plane Mirror Image
Figure 5 In this virtual image, the reflected light rays appear to come from behind the mirror, where the image forms. The distance from the image to the mirror is the same as the distance from the object to the mirror.

Convex Mirror Image
Figure 6 The passenger's side mirror on a car is convex. Light rays bend when they hit the surface of the mirror in such a way that the object appears smaller than it is.

Optical axis

Focal point

Concave Mirrors Just as a convex mirror is like the outside of a shiny bowl, a concave mirror is like the inside of the bowl. The surface of a **concave** mirror curves inward. **Figure 7** shows that the focal point of a concave mirror is on the reflecting side of the mirror. The image that forms from a concave mirror depends on whether the object is between the focal point and the mirror or farther away from the mirror than the focal point. If the object is farther from the mirror than the focal point is, then reflected light rays cross one another, and the image is inverted. This image is called a *real image*. If the object is between the focal point and the mirror, then the image is not inverted and is larger than the actual object. This image is called a *virtual image*. Large telescopes are built with mirrors. The 5.1-meter Hale telescope at Mount Palomar, in southern California, was the largest telescope in the world for more than 40 years.

✓ CHECK POINT **Classify** If a mirrored image is inverted, what type of image is it?

....

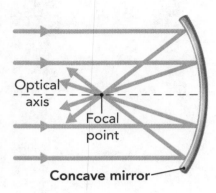

Mirror Images
Figure 7 The images formed by mirrors depend upon the shape of the mirror. Examine the diagram, and then identify the type of image in each example.

Optical axis

Focal point

Concave mirror

The object is located farther from the mirror than the focal point is. It forms a .... image.

The object is located between the mirror and the focal point. It forms a .... image.

Model It

Fun with Mirrors

In a fun house, mirrors are often used to change the appearance of objects.

SEP Develop Models Suppose you want to use a mirror to make a door look smaller and rounder. In the space below, draw the mirror and the door, along with the focal point. Label the mirror with the type of mirror it is.

Lenses

Light not only reflects, as it does with a mirror, but it also bends, or refracts. A lens is a curved piece of transparent material that refracts light. You may wear eyeglasses, which are lenses that correct your vision. Lenses are also used in devices designed to serve other functions, such as telescopes and cameras. Just like a mirror, a lens is either convex or concave, depending on its shape.

 VIDEO

Explore the effects of different lenses and filters in cameras.

Convex Lenses Look at **Figure 8** to see what convex lenses look like, how they refract light, and what type of image is produced. You can see that convex lenses are thicker in the middle and thinner at the edges. As light passes through the lens, it refracts toward the center of the lens. The more curved the lens is, the more the light refracts.

Academic Vocabulary
Student Discourse Have a class discussion about how comparing items differs from contrasting them.

A convex lens can produce either a virtual image or a real image depending on where the object is located relative to the focal point of the lens. If the object is between the lens and the focal point, then a virtual image forms. This image is larger than the actual object. You may have observed this when using a magnifying glass. If the object is farther away from the lens than the focal point is, then a real image forms. This image can be larger, smaller, or the same size as the object.

Compare a convex lens and a concave mirror. Both a convex lens and a concave mirror are designed to focus light, and the type of image formed depends on the location of the object compared to the location of the focal point.

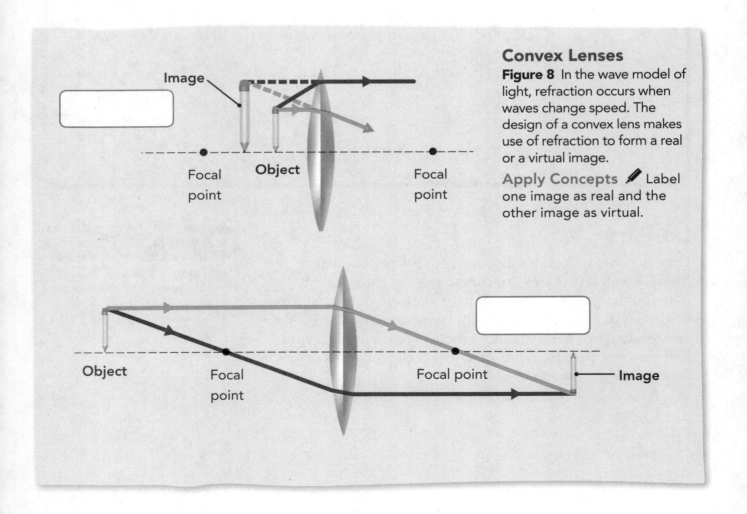

Convex Lenses

Figure 8 In the wave model of light, refraction occurs when waves change speed. The design of a convex lens makes use of refraction to form a real or a virtual image.

Apply Concepts Label one image as real and the other image as virtual.

Concave Lenses

Concave lenses are thinner at the center than they are at the edges. When light rays travel through the lens, the rays are bent away from the optical axis, so the rays never meet. Because the rays never meet, concave lenses form only virtual images, and these images are upright and smaller than the objects. **Figure 9** shows how concave lenses form images.

INTERACTIVITY

Predict the behavior of light rays as they encounter different objects and substances.

☑ **CHECK POINT** **Compare and Contrast** In what ways is a convex lens like a concave mirror? In what ways is it different?

....

....

....

....

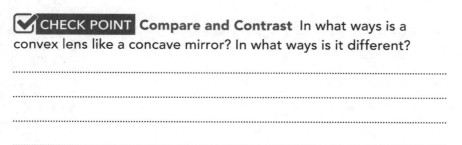

Object   Focal point   Image   Focal point

Focal point   Object   Image   Focal point

Concave Lenses

Figure 9 When looking through a concave lens, a virtual image forms that is always smaller than the object itself.

Apply Concepts ✎ After examining the diagrams, circle the photo in which the image is formed by using a concave lens.

1. **Classify** What kind of material transmits some light, making objects behind it appear blurry?

....
....
....
....
....
....

2. **Identify** A bird runs into the window of a building because it sees the reflection of the sky in the window. The sky does not appear distorted in this window. What type of mirror or lens is the window acting as? Explain your answer.

....
....
....
....
....
....

3. **SEP Design Solutions** When a person is nearsighted, an eyeglass lens is needed to bend light entering the eye away from the optical axis. What type of lens will do this?

....
....
....
....
....
....

4. **CCC Cause and Effect** Why do some rear-view mirrors in a car state, "Objects are closer than they appear"?

....
....
....
....
....

5. **SEP Construct Explanations** Suppose a movie director is filming on a set that should look like a hot desert. He wants the scene to appear warmer, so that the red and yellow tones are the most apparent. What color filters should he use? What color will the blue sky appear when he uses those filters, and why?

....
....
....
....
....
....
....
....
....
....
....

Lights! Camera!
ACTION!

A lighting designer plans how to light a stage or other performance space. The designer uses three factors—color, intensity, and motion—to light a show in the most effective way possible.

There are three primary, or basic colors. For pigments, the primary colors are red, yellow, and blue. In lighting, the primary colors are red, green, and blue. When the three primary colors are mixed in equal amounts, a painter ends up with black paint, but a lighting designer creates white light!

Lighting designers use several types of lighting instruments. For color, they may place a thin sheet of plastic polymer called a *gel* in a frame. Designers can combine colored gels to make other colors. For instance, a yellow gel and a cyan gel together produce red light. Gels are made in many colors, so a designer can combine them to produce any color you might imagine.

Lighting designers need a good understanding of physics and engineering, as well as of dramatic performance, to create effective displays. Lighting designers are called on to illuminate many kinds of events. Ice shows, filming movies, political appearances, and concerts are only a few situations in which lighting designers create the right mood and appearance.

▶ VIDEO

Explore how lighting designers use light to communicate with an audience.

📄 DOCUMENT

Go online to explore more science and engineering careers.

A lighting designer shines lights at different angles all around the stage to set a bright and lively mood for this concert.

MY CAREER

What kinds of decisions do you think lighting designers have to make? Is lighting design a career you could follow in California? Write down your thoughts and think about whether lighting design might be a good career for you.

 MS-PS4-1, MS-PS4-2

Evidence-Based Assessment

Bianca is helping the theater director at her school with lighting, sound, and set design for a school play. She will be choosing the materials that will be used on stage and on the walls of the theater. After she reads the script and makes observations inside the theater, she makes the following list of the factors to consider in her design.

- The echoes throughout the theater need to be reduced.

- The set should not reflect too much light into the audience's eyes.

- The only lights available are white, purple, and yellow. The filters available are red and blue.

- The blue sky on the set should appear black for Act 2.

Bianca draws a detailed illustration of her plan to show the theater director. She labels it with the materials she plans to use.

1. **Apply Scientific Reasoning** Bianca plans to shine a few spotlights on the sky for Act 2 and use a filter to change the color. Which filter should Bianca use on the white light to make the blue sky appear black?

A. a red filter

B. a blue filter

C. a white filter

D. no filter at all

2. **Identify Criteria** Which of the following considerations does Bianca need to take into account as she works on the set and lighting design? Select all that apply.

☐ Two different sets are needed for Act 2.

☐ The set materials should not be too shiny or glossy.

☐ Only the colors white, purple, and yellow can be used to paint the sets.

☐ The walls have hard surfaces that reflect sound waves.

☐ Only the white lights can be used for Act 2.

3. **SEP Use Models** Based on Bianca's illustration, did she choose the appropriate material on the walls for reducing echoes? Circle the words that explain your answer.

(No / yes). Felt will (absorb / reflect) sound waves. This will create (more / fewer) echoes throughout the theater.

4. **SEP Develop Models** As sound waves travel away from the speaker, their amplitudes and energy decrease. Where will the sound be the least intense? If you were to move the speaker, where would you place it, and why?

....

....

....

....

....

....

....

5. **SEP Design Solutions** Based on Bianca's criteria and model, which materials would you change on stage? Explain your reasoning.

....

....

....

....

....

....

....

....

....

Making Waves

How can you use a **model** to demonstrate what happens when **waves interact** with barriers or other waves?

Background

Phenomenon A wave breaker is a large wall made of rocks or concrete objects that extends into the ocean. Breakers often are built near beaches to make the water calmer for swimmers. These barriers help to diminish the force of incoming waves by scattering them and interfering with their movements.

In this lab, you will model the behavior of water waves and explain how the waves interact with each other and with objects in their paths. You will then decide on the best method and materials for reducing waves.

Materials

(per group)

- water
- plastic dropper
- metric ruler
- paper towels
- modeling clay
- plastic knife
- cork or other small floating object
- ripple tank (aluminum foil lasagna pan with mirror on the bottom)

Safety

Be sure to follow all safety guidelines provided by your teacher.

This rock barrier at Ocean Beach in San Diego, California, to block big waves and make the beach more enjoyable for swimmers.

Design an Investigation

☐ One way to generate waves is to squeeze drops of water from an eyedropper into a pan of water. How can you use the dropper to control how large the waves are?

....

....

....

☐ What questions will you explore in your investigation? Some questions to explore include:

- What happens when waves hit a solid surface?
- What happens when waves travel through a gap between two solid objects?
- How does a floating object react to waves?
- What happens when one wave meets another wave?

☐ Record any additional questions you hope to answer in your investigation.

....

....

....

☐ Design an experiment to show how waves behave when they interact with different objects or with each other. Write out a procedure. Then decide what information to record and design a data table to record your observations.

HANDS-ON LAB

ⁿ**Demonstrate** Go online for a downloadable worksheet of this lab.

Procedure

Data

Analyze and Interpret Data

1. **SEP Construct Explanations** What evidence supports the claim that the waves in the water are mechanical waves?

   ....

   ....

   ....

2. **CCC Cause and Effect** In what situations did you observe waves interfering with one another? How did it affect the amplitude of the waves?

   ....

   ....

   ....

   ....

3. **Claim** Which material and set-up was best for reducing waves? Which was the worst?

   ....

   ....

   ....

4. **Evidence** What evidence led you to your conclusions?

   ....

   ....

   ....

5. **Reasoning** Repetition is when you repeat a step of the procedure a few times to see if you get the same results. Did you use repetition in your experiment? Why or why not?

   ....

   ....

   ....

6. **SEP Design Solutions** Share your results with members of another group. What did they do differently? In what ways would you suggest that the other group members revise their procedure?

   ....

   ....

   ....

Information Technologies

Investigative Phenomenon
How can you demonstrate that digital signals are more reliable than analog signals?

MS-PS4-3 Integrate qualitative scientific and technical information to support the claim that digitized signals are a more reliable way to encode and transmit information than analog signals.

What do these tiny circuits do?

HANDS-ON LAB

uConnect Consider ways to represent the terms *continuous* and *discrete*.

What questions do you have about the phenomenon?

....

....

....

....

....

....

....

....

....

(1) Signals

HANDS-ON LAB

uInvestigate Explore how analog signals can be converted to digital information.

MS-PS4-3 Integrate qualitative scientific and technical information to support the claim that digitized signals are a more reliable way to encode and transmit information than analog signals.

Connect It!

✏️ **Circle the visual signal that is being used to communicate information.**

SEP Construct Explanations Why do you think the air marshal's signals are useful for communicating with a pilot on board an aircraft?

....

....

....

....

Signals and Information

An electric circuit can be used to power a device like a light bulb. However, circuits can also be used to send information. Think about a doorbell, which is usually a circuit. When someone presses a button outside a door, the circuit is complete and the electricity powers a bell that chimes. If you understand the meaning of the chime (a signal that someone is at the door), then you can respond by going to the door. For any signal to be understood, there needs to be agreement between the sender and the receiver about what the signal means. In some cases, the signal can be simple, such as a doorbell or basic hand signals, like the one the aircraft marshal is using in **Figure 1**. Others are more complex. For example, you are reading a specific sequence of letters and spaces on this page to learn about signals.

For much of the 1800s, people communicated with each other over great distances using electrical signals. Samuel Morse patented a version of the electrical telegraph in 1837, and by the Civil War in 1861, there were telegraph lines that carried Morse code from one side of the United States to the other.

HANDS-ON LAB

Compare and contrast analog and digital clocks.

Signaling
Figure 1 A member of the California Air National Guard uses visual signals to communicate with pilots.

Morse Code

Figure 2 In Morse code, combinations of short (dot) and long (dash) wave pulses are sent and each combination is translated into a letter.

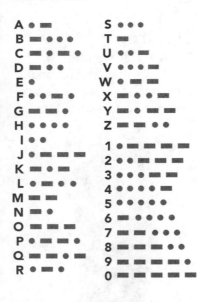

A •—	S •••
B —•••	T —
C —•—•	U ••—
D —••	V •••—
E •	W •——
F ••—•	X —••—
G ——•	Y —•——
H ••••	Z ——••
I ••	1 •————
J •———	2 ••———
K —•—	3 •••——
L •—••	4 ••••—
M ——	5 •••••
N —•	6 —••••
O ———	7 ——•••
P •——•	8 ———••
Q ——•—	9 ————•
R •—•	0 —————

Electronic Signals

An electrical telegraph is used to send Morse code as an **electronic signal**, information that is sent as a pattern in a controlled flow of current through a circuit. The telegraph turns the current on and off as the operator taps a device to close and open the circuit, as shown in **Figure 2**. In Morse code, a signal composed of short (dot) and long (dash) wave pulses stand for the letters of the alphabet and punctuation marks. A **wave pulse** is a pulse of energy. In Morse code, the letter A is sent and received as "•—", B is "—•••", and so on. This code can be used to send messages, but it is very slow.

Electronic signaling became more useful and widespread when inventors developed ways to transmit information without translating them into code. In 1876, Alexander Graham Bell patented the first telephone. In Bell's telephone, two people spoke into devices that were part of the same circuit. A microphone converted soundwaves in the air—a caller's voice—into electronic signals that would be carried to the receiver somewhere else. At the time, switchboard operators manually connected two telephones into the same circuit. Eventually, switchboards became fully automated.

Model It!

Be a Telegraph Operator

1. **CCC Patterns** Use the Morse code chart in **Figure 2** to decode the following four lines of code.

   •—— •••• •— — ....

   •• ••• ....

   ••—• ——— •—• ....

   •—•• ••— —• —•—• •••• ....

2. **SEP Use Models** ✏ Use Morse code to provide an answer to the message you decoded.

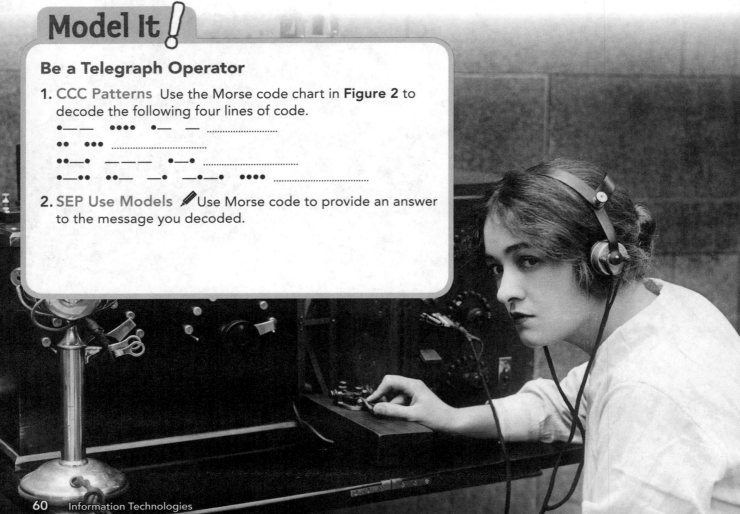

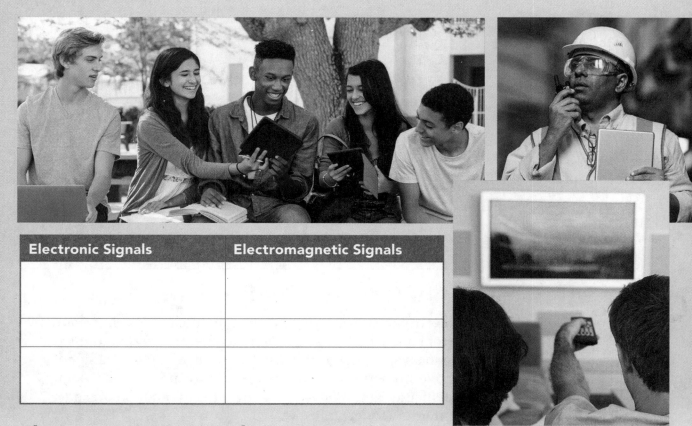

Electronic Signals	Electromagnetic Signals

Electromagnetic Signals

Information sent as patterns of electromagnetic waves such as visible light, infrared waves, microwaves, and radio waves are **electromagnetic signals**. Modern information technologies use a combination of electronic and electromagnetic signals. In 1895, the first radio station transmitted radio wave signals between two points without using an electric circuit. This launched wireless forms of communication that allowed messages to be transmitted across the globe. Wireless technologies, such as the ones shown in **Figure 3**, now dominate the telecommunications industry. Electromagnetic signals travel at the speed of light, which is much faster than the speed at which current flows through a circuit.

Different types of electromagnetic signals are used for different purposes. Modern mobile phones communicate using microwaves, which are in the ultra-high frequency (UHF) band of the electromagnetic spectrum. Submarines communicate underwater with extremely low frequency (ELF) waves. Optical fibers use visible and infrared light to transmit large amounts of information.

✓ CHECK POINT **Determine Central Ideas** What is an electronic signal?

....

....

From Wired to Wireless

Figure 3 The transition from wired to wireless telecommunications has allowed people to communicate and share information with each other with greater convenience, speed, and quality.

Compare and Contrast
✎ Complete the table to compare and contrast electronic and electromagnetic signals.

Types of Signals

Figure 4 Analog signals are continuous, whereas digital signals are discrete.

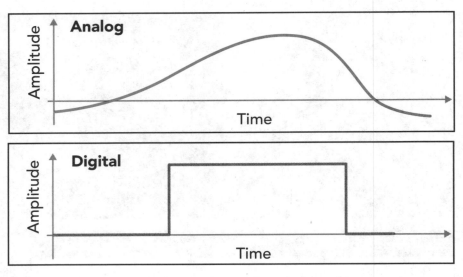

▶ **VIDEO**

Compare analog sound recording devices to newer digital technologies.

Literacy Connection

Summarize Texts
Underline the sentences that summarize the differences between analog and digital signals.

Analog and Digital Signals

Electronic and electromagnetic signals can carry information from one place to another in two different ways: as analog signals or as digital signals. Both analog and digital signals have strengths and weaknesses, but the power and flexibility of digital signals have made them the foundation of modern information technologies.

Analog Signals An **analog signal** allows for a continuous record of some kind of action (**Figure 4**). For example, when seismic waves from an earthquake cause the ground to move, a seismograph records that continuous motion as an analog signal. The advantage of analog signals is that they provide the highest resolution of an action by recording it continuously. But analog signals can be difficult to record. The signals processed by a seismograph must be recorded with ink on paper as a seismogram. Other examples of analog signals are the recordings of music on vinyl records. You can slow down a record and still hear continuous music. However, vinyl records scratch and warp very easily. Analog media also take up a lot of space, compared to digital media.

Digital Signals A **digital signal** allows for a record of numerical values of an action at a set of continuous time intervals (**Figure 4**). This results in a series of numbers. For example, a digital seismometer can record ground motion by recording the numerical value of the ground height at each second. This produces a list of numbers that shows the ground motion, second by second. The disadvantage of digital signals is that you do not have a record of any signals that occurred in between each sampling. One advantage is that once you have recorded the signal as a set of numbers, you can store it on a computer or other digital device. Digital recordings can also be edited easily by just changing the numbers.

Sampling Rate The quality of digital media depends on the length of the recording intervals. The term *sampling rate* refers to how often a signal is recorded or converted to digital code. More data are captured and recorded the more times the event is sampled (**Figure 5**). For example, a digital music file with a high sampling rate may sound richer and more detailed than a file with a lower sampling rate. The downside of a higher sampling rate is that the file size is larger.

Scientists and music producers have conducted tests with people to find a sampling rate that will produce digital music files that sound realistic without having more data than humans can perceive. If the sampling rate is too high and the files are too large, then the files will waste space on music players, mobile phones, computers, or storage services.

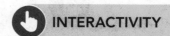

INTERACTIVITY

Compare analog and digital signals, and learn about signal noise.

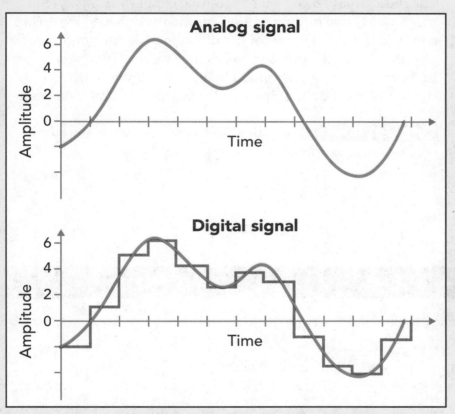

Analog-to-Digital Processing

Figure 5 When an analog signal is converted to a digital signal, what was continuous must be broken into discrete pieces. The higher the sampling rate, the closer the digital signal will come to the analog signal.

SEP Develop Models 🖊
Draw two digital versions of the original analog signal in the blank graphs: one based on sampling the analog signal 24 times, and the other based on sampling 32 times.

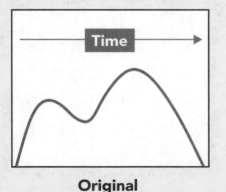

Original

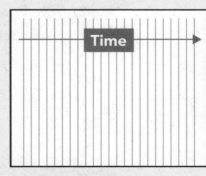

Sampled 24 times   **Sampled 32 times**

Investigate Explore how analog signals can be converted to digital information.

Binary Code

Figure 6 The binary codes, or bytes, for the first five letters of the alphabet are shown here. Notice that there are different codes for lowercase and uppercase letters.

a = 01100001 A = 01000001
b = 01100010 B = 01000010
c = 01100011 C = 01000011
d = 01100100 D = 01000100
e = 01100101 E = 01000101

SEP Interpret Data What would the code be for the word *Dad*?

Binary Signals Recall that Morse code has just two signals—dots and dashes—that are used in different combinations to communicate letters. Computers use a similar system called binary, which consists of ones and zeros. The information that we store on computers is encoded with binary, whether it's a song, a text document, or a movie.

Each number in binary code is a bit of information. Bits are arranged into groups of eight, called bytes. The code for each letter of the alphabet has its own unique byte, as shown in **Figure 6**. The code for a word consists of bytes strung together. For example, as the author wrote this page, a computer program translated the keyboard strokes for the letters in the word "*code*" into bytes.

01100011011011110110010001100101

The basic unit of a computer's storage capacity is the byte. A megabyte is one million bytes. This means one megabyte (MB) can hold a million letters of the alphabet. Digital storage has improved so much in recent years that we now use even larger units such as gigabyte (billion bytes) and terabyte (trillion bytes) to describe the storage capacities of our digital devices.

✓ **CHECK POINT** **Summarize Text** How are signals stored and processed on computers?

......

Math Toolbox

Cryptography

Cryptography is the study of codes. Use the chart in **Figure 6** to answer the following questions and "break" the codes.

1. **Draw Comparative Inferences** The binary code for the number 5 is 00110101. How does this compare to the code for *e*? What can you infer about the structures of these codes?

......

......

......

......

Transmitting Signals

Modern forms of communication involve the **transmission** of electronic or electromagnetic signals. Many transmissions are now in digital formats. In some cases, the transmission consists of an entire file, such as a digital song file saved to your phone. In other cases, the transmission is more like a broadcast, such as a live stream.

Sound Information Analog telephones transmit signals by first converting sound waves to electronic wave pulses. Those travel along wires to another phone, which converts the wave pulses back to sound waves. Modern mobile phones convert sound waves to digital data in the form of binary code. The data are transmitted as microwaves, which are converted back to sound waves by another mobile phone. If someone records and sends a voice message from one mobile phone to another, or to a computer, the process is basically the same. Sound waves are the initial signal and the ultimate product.

Academic Vocabulary

In your science notebook, record other uses of the term *transmission* in science. In those other contexts, what's being transmitted?

Digital Audio

Figure 7 To transmit a sound signal from one place to another, the signal must be processed and converted into different forms.

SEP Develop Models ✏ Complete the diagram by identifying the type of signals that are being transmitted.

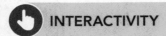

INTERACTIVITY

Model how the number of pixels affects the resolution of digital images.

Visual Information Photographs, printed documents, and other visuals can be digitized and transmitted as well. A digital visual consists of **pixels**, or small uniform shapes that are combined to make a larger image (**Figure 8**). The information that determines a pixel's color and brightness is coded in bytes. The more pixels that are used, the more bytes the digital image file will require. For example, a digital image that is meant to take up a few centimeters on a mobile phone screen may be far less than a megabyte, whereas an image that is meant to be shown on a high-resolution display or printed as a poster can be 50 megabytes or more. Just as audio engineers and music producers try to balance file size with detail that will be audible to human ears, visual artists and engineers must strike a balance too. They don't want their images to appear too "pixelated," but they don't want to waste device storage with too much detail either.

Model It

Model Digitized Signals

As shown in **Figure 8,** higher resolution images require larger file sizes than lower resolution images.

1. **SEP Develop Models** ✏️ Create a model of a low-resolution digital image. Use squares to represent each pixel and shade or color each square. Ask a partner if they can identify the subject of your image.

2. **SEP Use Models** What are some advantages and disadvantages to using images with fewer pixels?

....

....

....

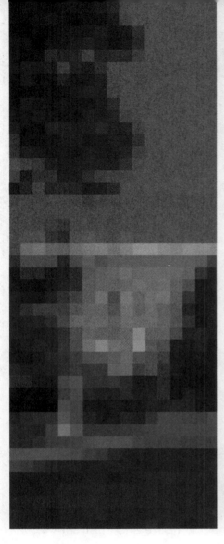

✅ CHECK POINT **Summarize Text** How are pixels used to capture and convey visual information with digital technology?

....

....

....

....

....

....

....

....

....

....

....

....

Pixels and File Size
Figure 8 The three images of the California State capitol are copies of the same file. The leftmost image has a low resolution and small file size. The middle image has higher resolution and a larger file size. The rightmost image has the highest resolution and largest file size.

🕐 MS-PS4-3

1. Identify Sound waves move from a guitar to a microphone. The microphone converts the sound waves to electronic wave pulses that are transmitted through a wire to a computer. The computer converts the wave pulses to a series of 1's and 0's. The 1's and 0's are packaged as a file and posted online for sale to the guitarist's fans. In this process, when were the signals digital?

....

....

....

....

....

....

....

....

....

2. SEP Use Mathematics If one letter of the alphabet is one byte, and the average word consists of five letters, how many words could be encoded in binary and stored on a 1-GB memory card?

....

....

....

....

....

....

....

....

....

....

3. Make Comparative Inferences How is the sampling rate used in recording digital music similar to the number of pixels in a digital image?

....

....

....

....

....

....

....

....

....

....

....

....

4. CCC Patterns Compare and contrast Morse code and binary code.

....

....

....

....

....

....

....

....

....

....

....

A LIFE-SAVING
Mistake

How do you create a tiny device that saves hundreds of thousands of lives? You engineer it! The story of Wilson Greatbatch shows us how.

The Challenge: To develop the first successful cardiac pacemaker.

Phenomenon In 1956, Greatbatch was working at the University of Buffalo, in New York, as an assistant professor in electrical engineering. He was building an electronic device to record the heart rhythms of cardiac patients. While tinkering with the circuitry, he made a mistake and put a resistor into the circuit that was the wrong size.

When Greatbatch added the resistor, he did not get the outcome he expected. The circuit periodically buzzed with electrical pulses that reminded the engineer of a human heartbeat.

Greatbatch's error turned out to be a happy accident. He realized that the device could help cardiac patients whose hearts beat irregularly. He used the idea to develop the first successful pacemaker, a device that delivers small electrical shocks to the heart muscle to keep it beating regularly and pumping blood normally.

INTERACTIVITY

Explore what makes up a pacemaker and how it works.

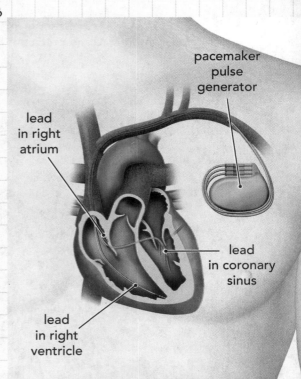

pacemaker pulse generator

lead in right atrium

lead in coronary sinus

lead in right ventricle

A pacemaker uses a pulse generator implanted below a patient's skin to send electric pulses to the heart. The pulses travel through wires called leads.

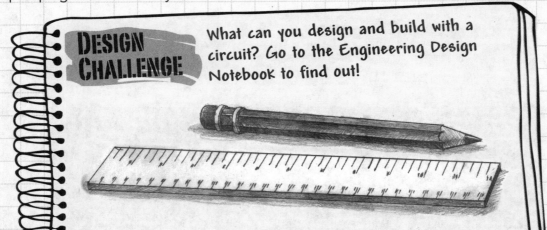

DESIGN CHALLENGE What can you design and build with a circuit? Go to the Engineering Design Notebook to find out!

Communication and Technology

HANDS-ON LAB

ᵘInvestigate Observe the structure of a vinyl record and predict how it functions.

MS-PS4-3 Integrate qualitative scientific and technical information to support the claim that digitized signals are a more reliable way to encode and transmit information than analog signals.

Connect It !

🖊 **Circle a symbol on the rock that represents an animal.**

Compare and Contrast How are these rock drawings similar to a computer or smartphone today? How are they different?

....

....

....

....

The Information Age

The invention of writing was one of the first examples of information technology. Using a sharpened stick or a finger and some kind of medium such as clay or a rock (**Figure 1**), people were able to record ideas, observations, and other information.

Fast forward to today. Information technology is everywhere, and there many forms and modes of writing. For example, one person typed the text on this page into a computer. The file was then sent via the internet to reviewers and editors. Edited text was then combined with the photograph in a different computer application. Finally, a file was sent to a printer, and a series of pages were put together as a book. What would have taken hours to inscribe in clay or rock can now be recorded and shared much faster, thanks to information technology. Modern **Information technology** consists of computer and telecommunications **hardware** and software that store, transmit, receive, and manipulate information. **Software** refers to programs that encode, decode, and interpret information, including browsers, apps, games, and operating systems. The invention of electronic computers around 1940 helped usher in the information age.

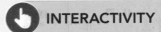
INTERACTIVITY

Discuss the encoding and decoding of information with classmates.

Academic Vocabulary
Hardware is an older term. What do you think "hard" refers to in the information technology usage of *hardware*?

....

....

....

California Petroglyphs
Figure 1 Tests have shown that some of the petroglyphs at Coso Rock Art District near Ridgecrest, California, were used to record information about 12,000 years ago.

Roger That!

Figure 3 Communications technologies all have one thing in common—they must move vast amounts of data in our digital world.

SEP Designing Solutions For each type of communications technology, identify a benefit and a drawback of using analog signals and digital signals.

Making a telephone call used to involve a large device mounted on a wall or in a booth, which was wired to a switchboard operator in another location, who would connect your call to a specific person by connecting two circuits. There was no "voicemail" system to record a message. The signal could be poor, making it difficult to hear each other. Nowadays, many people carry phones in their pockets that can connect to other people around the world.

For many years, radio and television broadcasts were transmitted using radio wave pulses. Analog televisions and radios depended on tall towers to broadcast signals over the air. In recent years, television has switched over to digital signal transmissions. Televisions can now handle high definition media.

Benefit

....

....

Drawback

....

....

Benefit

....

....

Drawback

....

....

Telecommunications satellites that orbit Earth can relay light and radio wave pulses that cannot be transmitted by wires or towers. Some satellites are used to broadcast television stations and other media, and others are used by government agencies and the military.

Benefit
....
....

Drawback
....
....

Fiber optic technology is based on glass or plastic cables that transmit light pulses at speeds around 200,000 kilometers per second. Fiber-optic cables can carry about a thousand times more information per second than standard copper cable.

Benefit
....

Drawback

The Internet is a complex set of interconnected networks that transmits information, largely through the World Wide Web. The Internet is usually accessed through an application called a browser, which allows people to navigate through the millions of pages. Internet connection used to require a cable plugged into a computer, but now many connections are achieved over wireless "WiFi" networks, or even mobile cellular networks.

Benefit
....
....

Drawback
....
....

HANDS-ON LAB

ıınvestigate Observe the structure of a vinyl record and predict how it functions.

Advantages of Digital Signals

Although they are not continuous signals, digital signals are more reliable and efficient overall than analog signals, for several reasons.

Compatibility with Computers

Computers process digital signals, and computers are everywhere—on laps and desktops, tucked in pockets, in car dashboards, and even on refrigerator doors. It's easier for computers and digital devices to do what we want them to do without having to convert analog signals first. Using digital signals is more efficient.

Noise

When an analog signal is transmitted, it can incorporate **noise**—random signals from the environment. This noise can then stay with the signal and alter the output. Static is an example of noise. Because digital signals consist of 0's and 1's, it is more difficult for noise to alter the signal, because binary code is essentially a choice between on and off. Unless noise causes a one to become a zero or vice versa, noise shouldn't affect how the digital signal is received or read.

Model It!

Noise? No Problem!
The first graph shows an analog signal accompanied by noise during transmission. The second graph shows a digital signal also accompanied by noise during transmission.

SEP Develop Models
Complete the models by drawing the received analog and digital signals to show how noise affects each one.

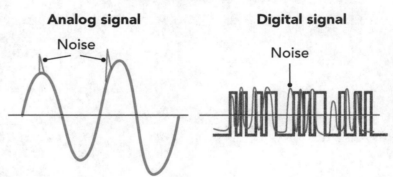

Original signal with noise

Analog signal

Noise

Digital signal

Noise

Received signal

Distortion caused by noise   Restored digital signal

Security Although digital signals are encrypted—hidden by binary coding—both analog and digital signals are vulnerable to security breaches. It's relatively easy for someone to tap into an analog phone line and listen to or record the conversation, because the signal is not encrypted. It's more difficult to access digital phone signals or communications, but hacking—stealing of digital information by breaking the codes—is on the rise. Tech experts are continually working to improve digital security.

Bandwidth As illustrated in **Figure 4**, the amount of information that can be transmitted and measured in bits per second is called **bandwidth**. Digital signals carry less information than comparable analog signals, so digital information technology solutions typically have greater bandwidth than analog solutions. For example, a cable that provides a home with television and Internet service can provide those services faster, and allow more data to be downloaded and uploaded, if it carries digital signals. Compression can help with bandwidth as well. For example, if a 1-gigabyte file can be compressed to a smaller file size for transmission and then uncompressed by a computer, the file should download faster.

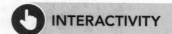

INTERACTIVITY

Research the advantages and disadvantages of analog and digital signals.

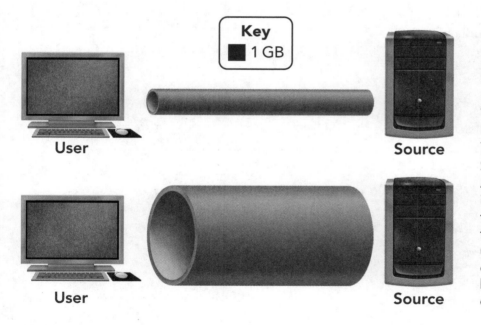

Key
■ 1 GB

User

Source

User

Source

Bandwidth

Figure 4 Narrow bandwidth means slower data transmission, which likely means slower download times.

SEP Develop Models
✎ Using the information in the key, model the transmission of 5 GB of data from each source to each user. Your model should demonstrate why narrower bandwidth results in slower download times.

☑ CHECK POINT **Cite Textual Evidence** Why are there so many different types of communications technology?

....

....

MS-PS4-3

1. Identify List five different technologies or types of hardware that are used today in communications.

....
....
....
....
....
....
....
....

2. CCC Cause and Effect Describe how increasing bandwidth and improving compression software can result in a higher quality of hardware and media of higher resolution.

....
....
....
....
....
....
....
....
....
....
....
....

3. Summarize What role does software play in information technology?

....
....
....
....
....
....
....
....

4. SEP Construct Explanations Explain why digital signals are somewhat harder to hack or spy on than analog signals.

....
....
....
....
....
....
....
....
....
....
....
....
....

From

"What Is Coding, Anyway?"

by **James Floyd Kelly**

Programs and software are examples of algorithms. In simple terms, an algorithm is a step-by-step procedure. A cake recipe, for example, is an algorithm. If you carefully follow the algorithm, then you should end up with a delicious cake. The same thing goes for an electronic device, such as a smartphone. When the phone's hardware follows the instructions in the software, then the phone will ring or vibrate when a call or text is received.

Most people think of computers when they think of algorithms. But algorithms are also found throughout nature. Researchers have recently discovered that some kinds of ants that forage for food use algorithms. These instructions are used to control the flow of ants leaving the colony in search of food, based on the number of ants coming into the colony. One of the researchers even found that the ant algorithm is similar to one used in some Internet technologies to control the flow of data!

CONNECT TO YOU

With a partner, discuss the communication technologies you rely on in a typical day. Choose one of the technologies and use the library or Internet sources to find out more about how the technology works.

MS-PS4-3

Evidence-Based Assessment

A friend of yours lives in a nearby town. The town needs to purchase new two-way radios for its emergency first responders. Town board members are considering replacing the two-way analog radios with digital radios.

However, the digital radios are more expensive. Board members want to know whether the increased costs will bring any benefits before they will vote to approve the measure. Many residents are opposed to spending additional money on new technology.

You and your friend research the issue and find the graph shown here, which compares the range and quality of analog radio signals with digital radio signals.

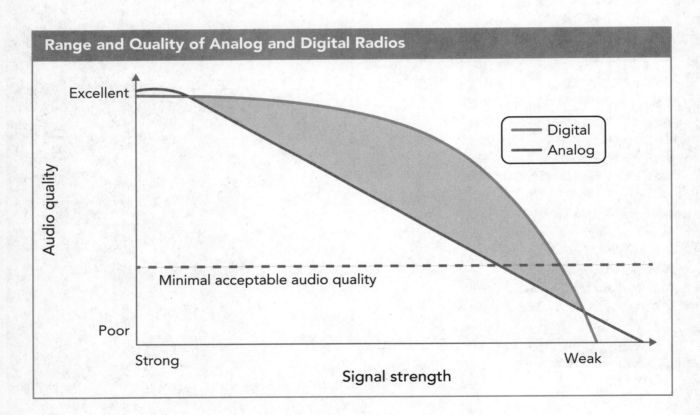

Range and Quality of Analog and Digital Radios

1. **SEP Interpret Data** What does the shaded part of the graph represent?
   A. area in which the audio quality of both radios is not affected by signal strength
   B. area of the digital radio's improved performance over the analog radio
   C. area in which there is no difference in quality between the analog and digital radios
   D. area of the analog radio's improved performance over the digital radio

2. **CCC Patterns** Which of the following statements about the data in the graph are correct? Select all that apply.
   ☐ The audio quality of the analog radio is slightly better with a very strong signal.
   ☐ The digital radio has improved audio quality with the very weakest signals.
   ☐ Both the analog and digital radio have almost the same quality with moderate signal strengths.
   ☐ The audio quality of the analog radios drops more sharply as signal strength weakens.

3. **Use Graphs** How are signal strength and audio quality related for both analog and digital signals? Circle the words which make the statement true.

   In general, audio quality (increases / decreases / stays the same) as signal strength decreases. The audio quality for analog and digital signals are (fairly different / about the same).

4. **SEP Cite Evidence** Use evidence from the graph to explain why the digital radio signals are more reliable than the analog radio signals.

   ....
   ....
   ....
   ....
   ....
   ....
   ....
   ....

5. **SEP Engage in Argument** What can your friend tell the town board members and residents to persuade them to purchase the digital radios?

   ....
   ....
   ....
   ....
   ....
   ....
   ....
   ....
   ....
   ....

Over and Out

How can you demonstrate that **digital** signals are a more reliable way to send **information**?

Background

Phenomenon The Center for Information Technology Education will soon open its doors to the public. The center houses a library for students and researchers, as well as a large multimedia theater and exhibit areas. The center has devoted space for hands-on exhibits where visitors can explore communication technology and its history. The center wants you to develop an interactive exhibit that compares and contrasts analog and digital signals. The exhibit's models will allow visitors to send a coded signal designed for each transmission method.

In this investigation, you will design models that help visitors recognize that digital signals are a more reliable way than analog signals to transmit data and information.

Materials

(per group)

- spring coil
- small light bulb and socket
- battery (9-volt or type C)
- electrical wire, 10 strips
- electrical switch

Safety

Be sure to follow all safety guidelines provided by your teacher. The Safety Appendix of your textbook provides more details about the safety icons.

1885

1920

1985

2015

In just over 125 years, telephone technology has evolved from large boxes with a lot of wires to small, wireless powerhouses.

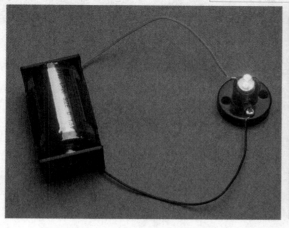
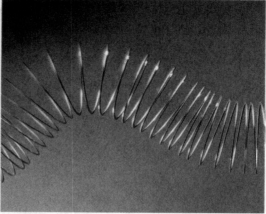

Design Your Exhibit Model

1. Plan the models you will use in the exhibit. Think about how you can use the available materials to represent two different communication systems: one that models how analog signals send information using continuous wave pulses and one that models how digital signals send information using discrete wave pulses. Consider the following questions as you plan and design your model:

   - Is the spring coil or an electric circuit a better choice to represent the continuous nature of analog signals?
   - Which of these materials is more appropriate to model the discrete nature of digital signals?

2. Develop a code that can be used for the analog system and another one that can be used for the digital system. The data you will transmit is a word made up of four letters: E, T, A, and S. You will need to create a code for each letter. Think about the following questions as you develop the codes:

   - How can you use continuous wave pulses of different amplitudes to represent each letter for the analog system?
   - How can you use discrete wave pulses to represent each letter for the digital system?

3. Sketch your models in the space provided and label the materials you will use. Include descriptions of how the models will operate. Then, complete the table with the codes you developed.

4. After getting your teacher's approval, carry out your investigation. One team member is the transmitter and the other member is the receiver. The transmitter should choose a word, refer to the code, and then transmit the word using the analog system. Repeat the process using a different word for the digital system. You may want to consider using commands to indicate the start and end of transmissions, such as "start transmission" and "end transmission." Run the trial again using the same procedure for each system.

HANDS-ON LAB

uDemonstrate Go online for a downloadable worksheet of this lab.

Model Sketches

Data Table and Observations

Letter	Analog Code	Digital Code
E		
T		
A		
S		

Analyze and Interpret Data

1. **SEP Use Models** Describe the results of your investigation and your observations about using each system to transmit information. Which system did you find easier to use? Which system was more accurate? Explain.

....
....
....
....

2. **Explain Phenomena** Think about the issue of signal noise. How could you incorporate this concept into your models? What effect do you think signal noise would have on the analog system? What effect might it have on the digital system?

....
....
....
....

3. **SEP Communicate Information** How do your models for the exhibit demonstrate what you've read about the reliability of digital signals versus analog signals?

....
....
....
....

4. **Identify Limitations** What are some of the challenges you faced as you designed your models and codes? What are some of the drawbacks or limitations of your models?

....
....
....
....
....
....

Human Impacts on the Environment

Investigative Phenomenon
What actions can we take to reduce our impact on Earth's systems?

MS-ESS3-4 Construct an argument supported by evidence for how increases in human population and per-capita consumption of natural resources impact Earth's systems.

MS-ETS1-4 Develop a model to generate data for iterative testing and modification of a proposed object, tool, or process such that an optimal design can be achieved.

EP&CIa Students should be developing an understanding that the goods produced by natural systems are essential to human life and to the functioning of our economies and cultures.

EP&CIb Students should be developing an understanding that the ecosystem services provided by natural systems are essential to human life and to the functioning of our economies and cultures.

EP&CIc Students should be developing an understanding that the quality, quantity, and reliability of the goods and ecosystem services provided by natural systems are directly affected by the health of those systems.

EP&CIIa Students should be developing an understanding that direct and indirect changes to natural systems due to the growth of human populations and their consumption rates influence the geographic extent, composition, biological diversity, and viability of natural systems.

EP&CIIb Students should be developing an understanding that methods used to extract, harvest, transport, and consume natural resources influence the geographic extent, composition, biological diversity, and viability of natural systems.

EP&CIIc Students should be developing an understanding that the expansion and operation of human communities influences the geographic extent, composition, biological diversity, and viability of natural systems

EP&CIIIc Students should be developing an understanding that human practices can alter the cycles and processes that operate within natural systems

EP&CIVa Students should be developing an understanding that the effects of human activities on natural systems are directly related to the quantities of resources consumed and to the quantity and characteristics of the resulting byproducts.

EP&CIVb Students should be developing an understanding that the byproducts of human activity are not readily prevented from entering natural systems and may be beneficial, neutral, or detrimental in their effect.

EP&CIVc Students should be developing an understanding that the capacity of natural systems to adjust to human-caused alterations depends on the nature of the system as well as the scope, scale, and duration of the activity and the nature of its byproducts.

EP&CVa Students should be developing an understanding of the spectrum of what is considered in making decisions about resources and natural systems and how those factors influence decisions.

What is happening to these trees?

HANDS-ON LAB

иConnect Explore ways that you can reduce the pollution you create.

What questions do you have about the phenomenon?

....

....

....

....

....

....

....

....

Quest PBL

How can you help your school reduce its impact on Earth's systems?

STEM ▸ **Figure It Out** The landfill used by your community is running out of space. The community must expand it or find other ways to deal with the trash. Your principal has decided to help the community by finding ways to reduce the school's trash output. In this problem-based Quest activity, you will evaluate the trash output at your school. You will then develop a plan to decrease that output through a combination of reducing, reusing, and recycling. As you work, you should anticipate objections to your plan. Finally, you will present your plan and work to implement it at your school.

NBC LEARN ▶ **VIDEO**

After watching the Quest Kickoff video, which explores the plastic items that end up in the ocean, think about the trash you generate. How can you reduce, recycle, or reuse your trash?

Reduce:

....

....

Recycle:

....

....

Reuse:

....

....

 INTERACTIVITY

Trash Backlash

 MS-ESS3-4

Quest CHECK-IN

IN LESSON 1

STEM ▸ How does the rate of trash generation affect landfills? Investigate how much trash is generated in an area of your school, and design and construct landfill models.

 INTERACTIVITY

More Trash, Less Space

Quest CHECK-IN

IN LESSON 2

How can landfills be constructed so they don't contaminate ground-water? Investigate how different designs will protect the water supply.

HANDS-ON LAB

Trash vs. Water

Quest CHECK-IN

IN LESSON 3

How is a landfill site chosen, and what laws regulate landfill use? Explore the stages of a landfill's life, and conduct research about laws that affect landfills.

 INTERACTIVITY

Life of a Landfill

According to the U.S. Environmental Protection Agency, Americans recycled only about 35 percent of their waste in 2014. Much of the rest of the waste ended up in landfills such as this one in Livermore, California.

Quest CHECK-IN

IN LESSON 4

How can everyone contribute to reducing waste at your school? Develop a plan to reduce trash output in at least one area of your school.

HANDS-ON LAB

Reducing Waste

Quest FINDINGS

Complete the Quest!

Refine and present your plan to reduce trash output at your school.

INTERACTIVITY

Reflect on Trash Backlash

① Population Growth and Resource Consumption

uInvestigate Examine how population growth affects the availability of natural resources.

MS-ESS3-4 Construct an argument supported by evidence for how increases in human population and per-capita consumption of natural resources impact Earth's systems.

Connect It !

✏️ **Draw a line to indicate where you think the city limits of Los Angeles were about 100 years ago.**

Apply Scientific Reasoning How do you think the amount of resources used by the human population of Los Angeles has changed in the past 100 years?

....

....

....

The Human Population

There are more humans living on Earth today than any time in our history. Human populations have fluctuated in the past, mostly due to environmental or climate conditions. Around 60,000 years ago, the human population was generally stable at around 600,000 individuals. A warming climate and improvements in hunting and fishing techniques resulted in a rapid increase to about 6 million humans over a few thousand years.

This population remained fairly constant until about 10,000 years ago, when agriculture and livestock breeding gave rise to steady, long-term population growth. This growth dropped occasionally during war, epidemics, or invasions, but maintained a steady climb until the 1700s. Since then, unprecedented population growth has occurred, with the human population reaching 1 billion by the early 1800s. In the last 300 years, the world population has increased tenfold. As of 2017, there were 7.5 billion people on Earth.

HANDS-ON LAB

Explore how food becomes a limiting factor when population size increases.

Reflect How has the population of your community changed in your lifetime? In your science notebook, describe some ways your community would be affected if the population were to suddenly increase or decrease.

Growth of a City

Figure 1 A little over 4 million people call the city of Los Angeles, California, home. The population has grown a great deal since the first Native American tribes settled there thousands of years ago.

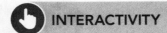
Academic Vocabulary

What other kinds of information might scientists need to estimate?

....

....

....

....

....

Population Changes

Population growth is determined by calculating the number of individuals who are born, die, or move into or out of an area. The number of births per 1,000 individuals for a certain time period is called the **birth rate**. On the other hand, the number of deaths per 1,000 individuals for a certain time period is called the **death rate**. When the rates of births and people moving into an area are greater than the rates of deaths and people moving out of an area, the population increases. Otherwise, the population decreases. In 2016, scientists **estimate** there were 280 births and 109 deaths every minute.

In early human history, birth rates and death rates were fairly balanced, which resulted in little change in the size of the human population. For most of human history, birth rates were only slightly higher than death rates, resulting in a slow, steady increase in population.

The graph in **Figure 2** shows human population growth beginning in 1750, around the start of the Industrial Revolution. Human population grew rapidly after the Industrial Revolution because the death rate began to decline. Advances in technology resulted in new farming and transportation methods that increased the availability of resources, such as food and clean water. Improvements in public health and general living standards also played a role in decreasing the death rate.

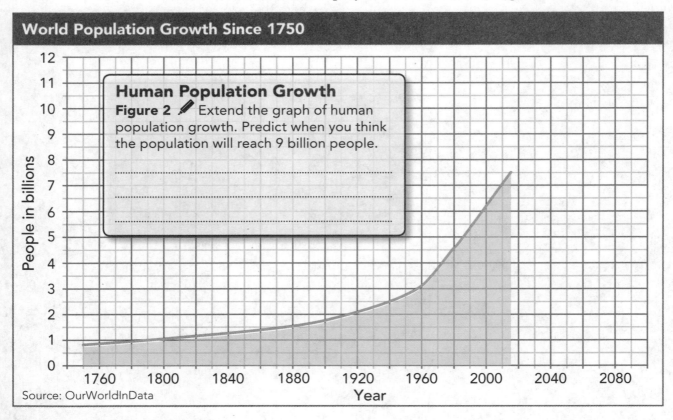

World Population Growth Since 1750

Human Population Growth

Figure 2 ✏ Extend the graph of human population growth. Predict when you think the population will reach 9 billion people.

....

....

....

Source: OurWorldInData

Population Growth Rate

Human population changes do not represent a straight line of increase on a graph. Instead the population increases more and more rapidly over time. This rate of change is called **exponential growth**—a growth pattern in which individuals in a population reproduce at a constant rate, so that the larger population gets, the faster it grows.

However, no living population can experience such extreme exponential growth for very long. Populations are limited by space and resources. Exponential growth will cease when a population reaches the upper limit of organisms its environment can support. At that point, the population will stabilize or possibly decline. Throughout history, human populations have experienced periods of growth and decline, depending on the conditions and resources available.

✓ CHECK POINT **Determine Conclusions** What would happen if the population growth rate reached zero?

....

....

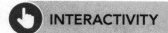

INTERACTIVITY

Learn about how human population growth affects Earth's systems.

Math Toolbox

Projected Growth Rates

The rate of human population growth is not the same all around the world. Experts use existing data to predict growth rates in different countries. Some areas may experience rapid growth, while others may have no growth or a decline.

1. **SEP Interpret Data** Which country represented has the highest population growth rate? Lowest?

....

....

2. **SEP Evaluate Evidence** What conclusions can you draw from the growth rates of Angola and Germany?

....

....

....

....

Country	Population Growth Rate (%)
Angola	1.9
Australia	1.0
Canada	0.7
Germany	−0.2
Haiti	1.3
Japan	−0.2
South Korea	0.5
United States	0.8
Venezuela	1.2

Source: CIA World Factbook, 2017 estimates

Investigate Examine how population growth affects the availability of natural resources.

Academic Vocabulary

What are some other words that have the same meaning as *constraint*?

....

....

....

Using Natural Resources

Earth provides many resources that humans rely on to live, such as energy sources, minerals, water, trees, and plants. These resources are needed by all organisms on Earth. Some resources, such as water, are part of systems that affect our planet's climate and other natural cycles.

Human Activity Industries and families alike rely on energy sources such as fossil fuels to provide electricity to power our lives. We use fuel to keep us warm in the winter and cool in the summer, to travel from place to place, and to grow and transport the food we eat. We use wood from trees and minerals that are mined from the ground to build everything from the tiniest computer chips to the tallest skyscrapers. Every human being relies on fresh, clean water to survive.

As the world's population grows, so does our demand for resources. Like the human population, many resources are not evenly distributed around Earth. For example, the availability of fresh, usable water varies in different locations on Earth. It is one of the factors that may act as a **constraint** on human activities in the near future. Currently, more than 700 million people do not have access to safe, clean water. This lack of clean water forces many individuals to consume unsafe water. Experts estimate that by 2025, nearly 1.8 billion people could be suffering from water scarcity.

Question It!

Mining Salt

Salt is not only a necessary part of the human diet, it is used in numerous industrial and agricultural applications. Most of the salt used today is mined from underground deposits.

SEP Ask Questions Develop a list of questions you would ask to help determine the relationship between human population growth and salt mining.

Impact of Agriculture
Figure 3 In order to grow food for people to eat, farmers use fertilizers and other chemicals. These chemicals often run off the land and pollute lakes, rivers, and the ocean.

CCC Cause and Effect What effect does farming food for a growing population have on the environment?

....

....

....

....

....

....

....

Impact on the Earth System The use of natural resources has both short and long-term consequences, positive and negative, for the health of people and for the natural environment. We need natural resources. But using resources reduces the amount of nonrenewable resources like fossil fuels. Also, obtaining many of these resources involves drilling, mining, or clearing Earth's surface, which damages the land. As some resources such as minerals or fossil fuels become scarce, humans dig deeper and disturb more areas to keep up with our growing population. Human consumption, or use, of resources creates waste. Untreated waste can harm the environment. Motorized vehicles burn petroleum and release chemicals that can cause **pollution**, the contamination of Earth's land, water, or air.

Human activities also affect other life on Earth. When we mine for a mineral or divert water for agriculture (**Figure 3**) we often destroy valuable habitats. Pollution in land and water habitats endangers the organisms that live there. Also, many organisms are over-exploited as food. When the number of humans grows beyond what the available resources can support, we reach the point of **overpopulation**. Human overpopulation and rising per-capita (per person) consumption of natural resources contribute to many environmental and social issues, including climate change, habitat loss, and human conflict. There may come a point at which Earth cannot adequately meet human needs at our current rate of resource use.

✓ CHECK POINT **Determine Conclusions** How does a growing population impact land, air, and water resources?

....

....

Literacy Connection

Determine Conclusions As you read, underline evidence in the text that supports your conclusions about how growing populations impact the environment.

INTERACTIVITY

Examine the different types of resources available on Earth.

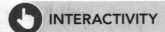

Balancing Needs

Science can identify problems and offer possible solutions, but it is up to individuals, governments, and international organizations to decide how to manage the impacts of a growing population. There are economic, social, and environmental costs and benefits which all must be weighed against one another (**Figure 4**). For example, humans use a variety of resources to produce electricity, from burning fossil fuels to building dams. No single method works in every situation, and there are benefits and costs to each.

The practice of using less of a resource so that it can last longer is called **conservation**. To ensure that future generations have access to the same resources we enjoy now, we need to use resources in ways that maintain them at a certain quality for a certain period of time. This practice is known as **sustainable use** of living resources. It gives resources time to recover and replenish themselves.

Addressing human impacts on the environment also requires engineering new solutions to our problems. These might include using desalination to counter water shortages, or advances in solar power, wind power, and other forms of renewable energy. As human populations continue to rise, the need for new ideas and solutions will increase.

CHECK POINT **Develop an Argument** Why is it important to conserve natural resources?

....

....

....

Harvesting Timber

Figure 4 We use timber, but there is an impact of our use on the environment. In the table, list the benefits and costs of logging.

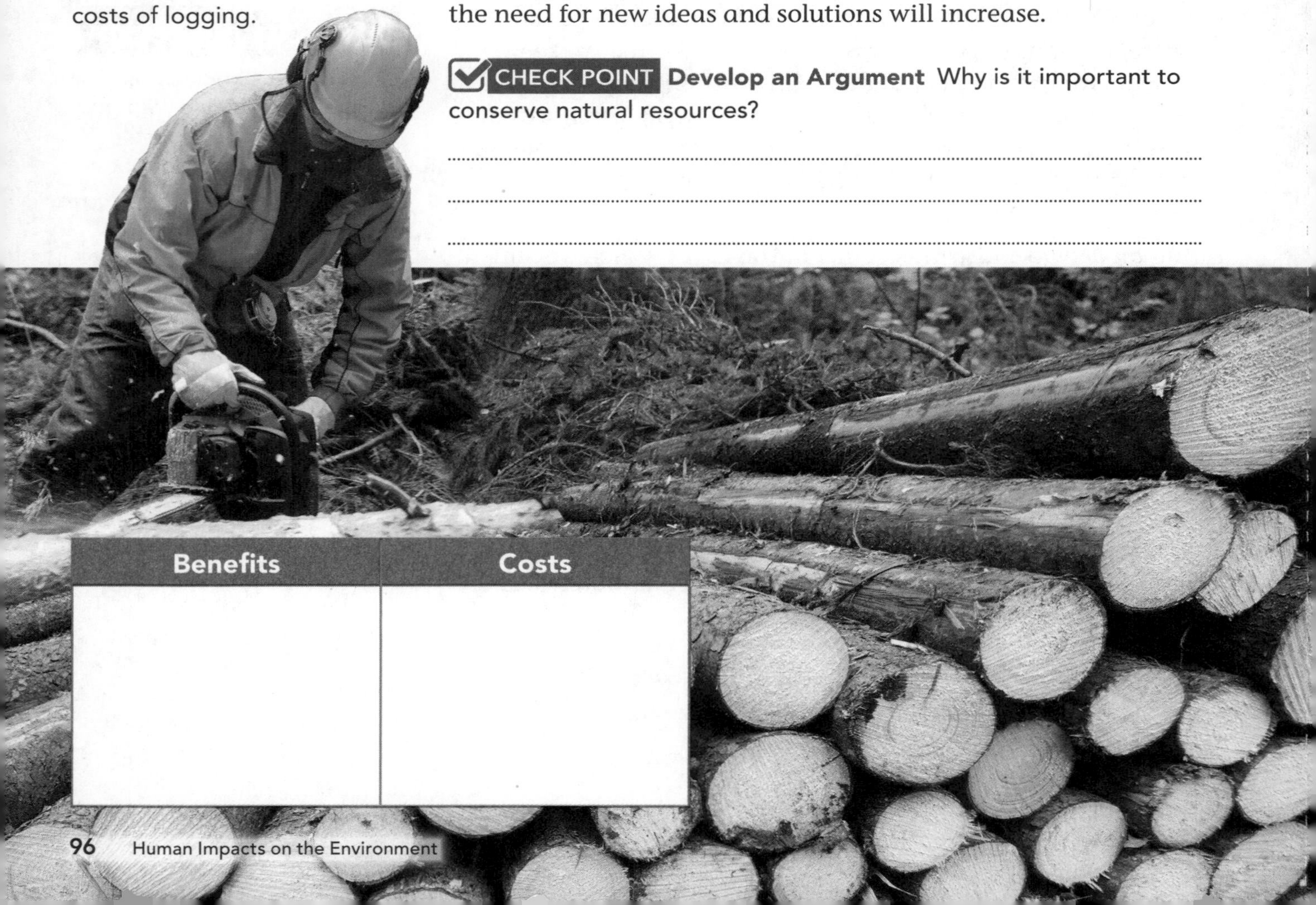

Benefits	Costs

☑ LESSON 1 Check

1. SEP Cite Evidence What factors limited human population growth in the past?

....
....
....
....

2. CCC Cause and Effect How did the Industrial Revolution affect human population growth?

....
....
....
....
....

3. SEP Engage in Argument What actions should humans take to conserve natural resources?

....
....
....
....

Use the graph to answer questions 4 and 5.

Human Population 1750–2020

4. CCC Evaluate Proportions What was the approximate population growth per year from 1800 to 1925? What was the approximate growth rate from 1925 to 2000? What is the ratio between the two rates?

....
....
....

5. Use Ratios Suggest two explanations for the ratio relationship you described in question 4.

....
....
....

Quest CHECK-IN

In this lesson, you learned how human population has changed over time and how human population growth impacts Earth's systems.

Connect to the Environment Why is it important to consider human population growth when developing strategies for dealing with pollution?

....
....
....
....
....

👆 INTERACTIVITY

More Trash, Less Space

Go online to learn about the total volume of trash generated in the United States and to determine how much trash is generated at your school.

②　Air Pollution

HANDS-ON LAB

ｕInvestigate Evaluate how different types of pollution affect air and water clarity.

 MS-ESS3-4 Construct an argument supported by evidence for how increases in human population and per-capita consumption of natural resources impact Earth's systems.

Connect It !

🖊 **Circle each mode of transportation that causes air pollution.**

SEP Construct Explanations How do these different forms of transportation pollute the air?

....

....

Make Predictions What is the benefit of walking or riding a bike?

....

....

Causes of Pollution

You are surrounded by air. Air is a mixture of nitrogen, oxygen, carbon dioxide, water vapor, and other gases. Almost all living things depend on these gases to survive. These gases cycle between the biosphere and the atmosphere. The cycles guarantee that the air supply will not run out, but they don't ensure that the air will be clean.

Pollution The contamination of Earth's land, water, or air is called pollution. Pollution is caused by liquids, chemicals, heat, light, and noise. Pollution can have short-term and long-term negative consequences on the environment and on the health of living organisms, including people.

Humans affect the levels of pollution by using natural resources and manufactured products. For example, **Figure 1** shows how the burning of gasoline pollutes the air. In addition, when coal and oil-based fuels are burned to generate electricity, carbon dioxide and sulfur dioxide are released into the air.

Types of Pollution A specific, identifiable pollution source is called a **point source**. A sewer that drains untreated wastewater into a river is an example of a point source.

A **nonpoint source** of pollution is widely spread and cannot be tied to a specific origin. For example, the polluted air around big cities is caused by vehicles, factories, and other sources. Because it is difficult to identify the exact source of the pollution, that pollution has a nonpoint source.

☑ **CHECK POINT** **Determine Central Ideas** What is the difference between point and nonpoint sources of pollution?

....

....

....

HANDS-ON LAB

Explore how particles move through the air.

Reflect What might be some short-term and long-term impacts of breathing polluted air?

Different Sources of Pollution

Figure 1 Pollution can occur naturally or through human activities. Sometimes the level of pollution is so great that it harms people.

Forest fires

Industrial emissions

Motor vehicle emissions

Livestock

Sources of Air Pollution

Figure 2 ✏ Circle the natural sources of pollution. Mark an *X* on the human-made causes of pollution.

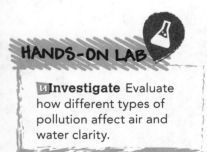

HANDS-ON LAB

и**Investigate** Evaluate how different types of pollution affect air and water clarity.

Outdoor Air Pollution

The air you are breathing is a combination of different gases. If you are in the mountains, the air might feel fresh and crisp. If you are at the shore, you might smell the salt water. In large cities, however, the air might not be as refreshing. Air pollution can be a big problem in areas where there are a lot of factories or a lot of people.

Emissions Many years ago, the main source of air pollution was the smoke being pumped out of factories. You have probably seen images of these **emissions**, or pollutants that are released into the air, as the dark smoke coming out of a factory's tall chimneys. This smoke is loaded with chemicals that mix with the gases in the air. However, today, most air pollution is released from coal-fired power plants and from motor vehicles, as shown in **Figure 2**. Emissions often contain carbon dioxide, which is also a pollutant. The increasing level of carbon dioxide is the primary contributor to the rise in average global temperatures over the past century.

Not all air pollution is caused by people. There are also some natural causes of air pollution, such as forest fires and volcanic eruptions. For example, the Hawaiian volcano Kilauea releases nearly 1,500–2,000 tons of harmful sulfur dioxide into the atmosphere each day during eruptions. However, human activities emit more than ten times as much sulfur dioxide and more than one hundred times as much carbon dioxide as all volcanoes combined.

Smog

If you live in a large city, chances are you have heard the term "smog alert." This is a warning to alert you that the amount of air pollution may make it difficult to breathe outdoors. Smog forms when certain gases and chemicals react with sunlight. This results in a thick, brownish haze that hovers over a city. Smog can cause breathing problems and diseases of the eyes and throat.

The **primary** source of smog is the emissions of cars and trucks. Among these emissions are chemicals called hydrocarbons and nitrogen oxides. These gases react in the sunlight to produce a form of oxygen called **ozone**. Ozone is toxic to humans, and it causes lung infections and harms the body's immune system.

Under normal conditions, air near the ground is heated by Earth's surface and rises up and away from the surface. Pollutants in the air are carried up into the atmosphere by the rising air. However, under certain weather conditions called temperature inversions, the normal circulation of air is blocked. As **Figure 3** shows, cool air becomes trapped below a layer of warm air during an inversion. This keeps the pollutants trapped near Earth's surface and causes them to become more concentrated and dangerous.

✓ CHECK POINT **Cite Textual Evidence** What are the main sources of air pollution and how do they cause smog?

....
....
....

Academic Vocabulary
Write a sentence using the word *primary*.

....
....
....

Temperature Inversion
Figure 3 ✏ Complete the image on the right by shading in the air pollutants to show how they are trapped during a temperature inversion.

Normal conditions
Cold Air
Cool Air
Warm Air

Temperature inversion
Cold Air
Warm Air
Cool Air

Literacy Connection

Cite Textual Evidence
As you read, underline the statements that support the idea that acid rain causes damage to living and nonliving things.

Acid Rain Precipitation that is more acidic than normal because of air pollution is called **acid rain**. When coal and oil are burned, they produce nitrogen oxide and sulfur dioxide gases. These gases are then released as emissions and react with the water vapor in the air to produce nitric and sulfuric acids. These acids become part of rain, snow, sleet, or fog.

When acidic precipitation falls to Earth's surface, it has damaging effects, as shown in **Figure 4**. As water and soil become more acidic, organisms will die off. Acid rain can also remove nutrients and minerals from the soil, affecting plant growth. Sometimes the effects of acid rain can be reversed by adding chemicals that neutralize the acid, but this is very expensive.

Acid rain also causes damage to nonliving things. The acid reacts with metal and stone of buildings, cars, and statues. It can cause metal to rust at a faster rate and causes the chemical weathering of stone. The effects of acid rain on these materials are irreversible.

☑ CHECK POINT **Write Arguments** Suppose your town government does not think that outdoor air pollution is a problem. What evidence could you use to convince the local government that air pollution is harmful to people and the environment?

....

....

....

....

....

Effects of Acid Rain

Figure 4 Acid rain can damage nonliving things as well as living things. Explain how acid rain might affect the trees in a forest.

....

....

....

....

....

Sources of Indoor Pollutants

modern building materials
outdoor air pollution
pet hair
molds and bacteria
fireplaces and woodburning stoves
cleaning products
paints and solvents
cigarette smoke
radon

Indoor Air Pollution
Figure 5 ✏ Underline the indoor pollutants that are human-made. Circle the pollutants that occur naturally.

Indoor Air Pollution

Sometimes the quality of the air inside a building can be just as bad as the air outside. There are several things that can contribute to indoor air pollution, as shown in **Figure 5**. Some of these can be human-made, while others occur naturally.

Allergens Obvious sources of indoor air pollution include dust, mold, and pet hair. These factors, while quite common, usually affect only people who are sensitive to them. Other sources of indoor air pollution include fumes from glues, paints, and cleaning supplies and tobacco smoke from cigarettes or cigars. These can affect everyone in the home.

Indoor Gases Radon and carbon monoxide are two harmful pollutants often found in homes or other buildings. Radon is a colorless, odorless gas that is radioactive. It forms underground from the decay of certain rocks. Radon enters a home through cracks in the foundation. Breathing this gas over long periods of time can cause lung cancer and other health issues.

Carbon monoxide forms when fuels such as oil, gas, or wood are burned. Breathing carbon monoxide causes respiratory issues, nausea, headaches, and even death.

The best way to protect against carbon monoxide is to install detectors near sleeping areas. These devices alert homeowners if concentrations get too high.

▶ **VIDEO**

Explore the misconception that indoor spaces do not suffer from air pollution.

☑ CHECK POINT
Integrate With Visuals
What are some ways to reduce the amount of indoor pollution in your home?

103

MS-ESS3-4

1. **Determine Differences** What is the difference between "helpful" and "harmful" ozone?

....
....
....
....

2. **Evaluate Reasoning** Why is the use of fertilizers on lawns in residential areas an example of a nonpoint source of pollution?

....
....
....

3. **SEP Provide Evidence** How does burning fossil fuels affect indoor air pollution?

....
....
....
....
....

4. **CCC Cause and Effect** What effect does burning fossil fuels during manufacturing and energy production have on outdoor air pollution?

....
....
....
....
....
....

5. **Construct an Argument** What evidence supports the claim that walking and biking to work would have a positive effect on air pollution?

....
....
....
....
....
....

Quest CHECK-IN

In this lesson, you learned how humans affect Earth's systems by producing different forms of air pollution. You also learned how we are working to reduce the impact of air pollution.

SEP Evaluate Evidence Why is it important to work toward reducing activities that contribute to air pollution?

....
....
....
....
....
....

HANDS-ON LAB

Trash vs. Water

Go online to download the lab to design and construct a model of a landfill.

Global to Local

MS-ESS3-4, EP&CIa, EP&CIb, EP&CIc, EP&CIIa, EP&CIIb, EP&CIIc, EP&CIVa, EP&CIVb, EP&CIVc, EP&CVa

Reducing
Climate Change
Together

Climate change is a global issue. Warming temperatures will change weather patterns, raise ocean levels, and rapidly change ecosystems worldwide. But solutions begin locally. The effects of changing climate include both short and long-term consequences. These include organisms that cannot adapt, and can therefore no longer provide food and ecosystem services for human communities. In 2015, Governor Brown of California issued an Executive Order to reduce greenhouse gas (GHG) emissions to 40% less than 1990 levels by 2030. California hopes to achieve that vision by reaching the following goals:

- Increase renewable electricity to 50%
- Double energy efficiency savings at existing buildings
- Reduce short-lived climate pollutants, such as: methane, soot, and hydrofluorocarbon propellants
- Reduce petroleum use by vehicles by 50%
- Reduce GHG emissions from land
- Safeguard California from droughts, floods, wildfires, and any negative impact that may result from climate change

California's state government is also working with other governmental agencies on a global level. Its Intergovernmental Working Group for the Climate Action Team coordinates and implements work with other states, countries, and areas interested in reducing air pollution and greenhouse gas emissions. Climate change is a global problem. It is important for local, state, and national governments to work together to develop and complete plans to reduce GHG emissions.

MY COMMUNITY

What are communities in California doing to reduce climate change? Explore the local tab of the California Climate Center website to find out.

The use of more hybrid and zero-emission vehicles, such as this electric bus, is essential to California reaching its 2030 greenhouse gas reduction goal.

ZERO EMISSION VEHICLE

3 Impacts on Land

uInvestigate Examine the impacts of mining.

MS-ESS3-4 Construct an argument supported by evidence for how increases in human population and per-capita consumption of natural resources impact Earth's systems.

Connect It!

✏️ **Identify and label one renewable resource and one nonrenewable resource shown in the image.**

CCC Cause and Effect What impact do you think the overuse of certain resources might have on Earth's ecosystems?

....

....

Land as a Resource

Did you drink water, turn on a light, or ride in a bus today? All of these activities, and many more, depend on Earth's **resources**. Anything we use that occurs naturally in the environment is called a **natural resource**. As **Figure 1** shows, natural resources include organisms, water, sunlight, minerals, and soil.

A **renewable resource** is either always available or is naturally replaced in a relatively short time. Some renewable resources, such as wind and sunlight, are almost always available. Other renewable resources, such as water and trees, are renewable only if they are replaced as fast as they are used.

Nonrenewable resources are resources that are not replaced within a relatively short time frame. Metals and most minerals are nonrenewable. Oil and coal are also nonrenewable resources. Fossil fuels such as oil and coal form over millions of years from the remains of organisms. At the rate humans are using fossil fuels, over time, they will be used up soon. All human activity that involves resources has short and long-term consequences that can be either beneficial or harmful for the health of humans. Resource use always has harmful effects on the environment.

While it does not cover as much of the planet's surface as water, land is also a vital resource. Humans use its many resources to survive. As **Figure 2** will show, it is used to grow food, obtain raw materials, and provide shelter.

Academic Vocabulary

A resource is not limited to a material, such as water or trees. What other kinds of resources do you rely on in your life?

....

....

....

....

Reflect What are some renewable and nonrenewable resources that you use? In your science notebook, describe these resources.

Natural Resources

Figure 1 As this image of a windfarm in Los Angeles, California, illustrates, human activity draws on different types of natural resources, both renewable, such as wind, and nonrenewable, such as gasoline.

Agriculture Land provides most of the food people eat. The use of land to produce food is called agriculture. Many areas of the world are not suitable for farming. New farmland is often made by draining wetlands, irrigating deserts, or deforestation. **Deforestation** is the removal of forests to use the land for other reasons. This process destroys the habitats of organisms living in these places.

Mining The metals and plastics used to make items such as televisions, cellular phones, building materials, and cars are mined from below Earth's surface. Metals and other resources are obtained through a type of mining called strip mining. Strip mining removes the top layer of dirt, exposing the minerals or ore underneath. When heavy winds and rains come, they can wash soil and land away. With it go all the nutrients it contains. It can take thousands of years for soil to be replaced.

Development Where do you live? It is a good bet that you live in a structure somewhere on the land. Whether it is a house, a camper, or an apartment building, the space your home takes up was once a habitat for other organisms. As the human population grows, more and more land is developed and built up with human structures, changing the habitat and often forcing organisms to find habitat elsewhere.

☑ CHECK POINT

Cite Textual Evidence
Which statements from the text support the idea that land is an important resource? Underline them.

clear-cutting

strip mining

development

Land Use
Figure 2 Humans use land in many different ways. How do increases in human population impact Earth's systems?

....

....

....

....

Importance of Soil Management

Healthy, fertile soil is essential for the success of agriculture because it contains the minerals and nutrients that plants require. Soil absorbs, stores, and filters water, which is also necessary for plant growth. Organisms living in soil, such as bacteria, fungi, and earthworms, break down the wastes and remains of living things and return them to the soil as nutrients.

Structure of Soil If you take a shovel and dig a hole in the ground, you will encounter several layers of soil, such as those shown in **Figure 3**. The first layer is called the litter. This top layer is where dead leaves and grass are found.

The next layer is called the topsoil. Topsoil is a mixture of nutrients, water, air, rock fragments, and dead and decaying organisms. Moving further down, the shovel will hit the subsoil. This layer contains the same water and air as the topsoil, but there are more rock fragments and fewer plant and animal remains here.

Underneath the subsoil is the layer of bedrock. This is the layer that makes up Earth's crust and is the basis for new soil. As time passes, water dissolves the rock, and its freezing and thawing action cracks and breaks apart the bedrock. Plant roots also help to break the bedrock by growing into cracks and then expanding. Animals such as earthworms and moles also help in the process. And as dead organisms break down, their remains contribute to the mixture of new soil.

Soil Layers
Figure 3 🖉 Fertile soil is made up of several layers. Label each layer of soil in the photo: *bedrock, litter, subsoil, topsoil.*

Plan It!

Community Considerations

CCC Cause and Effect Suppose you are part of a group that is converting an abandoned lot into a community garden. You need to plan the garden to avoid damaging the local environment further. What harmful effects should you consider and how can you minimize them?

....

....

....

....

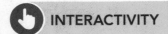

INTERACTIVITY

Explore how agriculture has affected soil and land.

Erosion Without soil, life on land could not exist. Soil takes hundreds of years to form. Therefore, every effort must be made to protect Earth's soil. Sometimes, natural forces cause soil loss. Forces such as wind, water, and ice move particles of rocks or soil through a process called **erosion**.

Usually, plant roots growing deep into the soil help to hold it in place. Human activities such as mining, logging, construction, and farming increase erosion by taking away these plants and exposing the soil to wind and precipitation. With nothing to anchor them in place, soil particles easily move. Human activities cause erosion to happen at a much faster rate than naturally-ocurring processes do. **Figure 4** shows some examples of natural and human-caused erosion.

Erosion

Figure 4 ✎ Check the image that shows naturally-ocurring erosion.

CCC Cause and Effect How did different events cause these areas to form?

....

....

....

....

....

....

....

....

Nutrient Depletion Plants make their own food through photosynthesis, but they need to take in nutrients such as nitrogen and phosphorus. Decomposers in the soil break down dead organisms, which add these and other nutrients to the soil. If a farmer plants the same crops in a field every year, the crops may use more nutrients than decomposers can supply. This leads to nutrient depletion; the soil is not adequately fertile. Nutrient depletion can directly affect humans. Crops grown in nutrient-poor soil often have less nutritional value.

Farmers add fertilizers to the soil to provide the needed nutrients. This can produce abundant, nutritious crops, but can also cause damage when rain carries the fertilizers into nearby bodies of water. Farmers often manage the soil by allowing it to sit for a season or two in between plantings. This allows the remnant crops to decompose, which replenishes the soil with nutrients.

Desertification When the soil in a once-fertile area loses its moisture and nutrients, the area can become a desert. The advance of desert-like conditions into areas that were previously fertile is called **desertification**.

One cause of moisture loss is drought. During these prolonged periods of low precipitation, plants, including crops, will dry up or not grow at all. Allowing livestock to overgraze grasslands and cutting down trees without replanting the area can also result in desertification. Without plant roots to hold the soil together, erosion of fertile topsoil will occur. Plant roots also carry water deeper into the soil, so it doesn't dry out as quickly.

From 2010 to 2016, the state of California experienced a severe drought. The people of California took preventive actions to avoid desertification. The state introduced mandatory water restrictions and regulations on the use of groundwater. Farmers also reduced the growing of certain crops to lessen the need for extensive irrigation.

Avoiding desertification

Figure 5 During California's most recent drought, strong leadership and cooperation of citizens helped prevent the spread of conditions like those seen here at the South Lake Reservoir near Bishop.

☑ CHECK POINT **Translate Information** In addition to precipitation, what could help reverse the conditions in **Figure 5**?

....

....

....

Causes of Land Degradation

Degraded land is in danger of desertification. Scientists estimate that there are at least 79.5 million hectares of degraded land in North America. The graph shows the causes.

Analyze Proportional Relationships How many more hectares were degraded by agricultural activities than by deforestation? Show your work.

....

....

....

....

....

....

Degraded Land in North America

7.7% 5.4% 52.1%

79.5 Million hectares

34.8%

- ■ Agricultural activities
- ■ Overgrazing
- ■ Overexploitation of vegetation for domestic use
- ■ Deforestation

SOURCE: United Nations Environment Programme

VIDEO

Learn more about what happens when you throw something "away."

Student Discourse

With a partner, discuss why it may be that capped landfills can be used for some purposes but not others.

Land Reclamation

Figure 6 ✏ These pictures show a mine that was reclaimed to include a stream. Add numbers to put these pictures in chronological order.

SEP Construct Explanations Explain what happened to the land in these pictures.

....

....

....

....

Landfills When you are asked to take out the garbage, where does it go once it leaves your curb? Today much of the solid waste, construction debris, and agricultural and industrial waste we produce is buried in holes called landfills. These areas are designed to protect the surrounding areas from soil and water pollution. If landfills are not managed correctly, they can harm the environment. Materials from waste can leak into the groundwater, making it toxic to drink.

Once a landfill is full, it is covered with soil heavy in clay to keep rainwater from entering the waste. These "capped" landfills can be reclaimed as locations for parks and sports arenas. Landfills take up large spaces that can never be used again for most human uses, including agriculture and housing.

Land Reclamation It is sometimes possible to restore soil that has been lost to erosion or mining. This process of restoring land to a more productive state is called land reclamation. Land reclamation could involve trucking in soil from another area. Sometimes mine operations reclaim land by storing the soil that they remove from a site, then putting it back after mining operations cease. Land reclamation can restore farming areas as well as wildlife habitats (see **Figure 6**). Land reclamation is very expensive and difficult. It is much harder to bring back damaged land than it is to protect and conserve those resources before they become damaged.

☑ **CHECK POINT** **Draw Evidence** How do human actions impact land? Give one positive and one negative impact.

....

....

....

Wetlands

A wetland is an area in which water covers the soil for all or most of the year. They are found in all climates and on all continents except Antarctica. Other terms you may have heard for wetland include bog, marsh, and swamp.

Figure 7 shows how wetlands support both land and aquatic ecosystems. They serve as breeding and nursery grounds for many organisms, provide habitats to many species of plants, and are feeding sites for many birds, mammals, and fish.

Human activities greatly impact wetlands. The development of homes, businesses, and roads requires controlling the flow of water through these areas. But altering the flow of water in a wetland changes the ecosystem and destroys unique habitats. It can also lead to increases in erosion, flooding, and the pollution of water and soil. Wetland soil acts as a natural "sponge" to collect water. Without wetlands, the large amounts of rain produced by severe storms, such as hurricanes, would flow directly into rivers or populated areas. Wetlands help to protect the quality of water by trapping excess sediments and pollutants before they reach the groundwater or waterways.

☑CHECK POINT **Integrate With Visuals** How would filling in a wetland to create a field affect the surrounding environment?

....

....

....

Literacy Connection

Cite Textual Evidence
When you write an argument, it should be based on factual evidence, not opinions. As you read, underline the evidence that supports the idea that human activities negatively affect the land.

How Wetlands Work
Figure 7 🖉 Wetland plants, soil, and bacteria protect surrounding aspects. Circle the aspects of the wetland that provide benefits to humans.

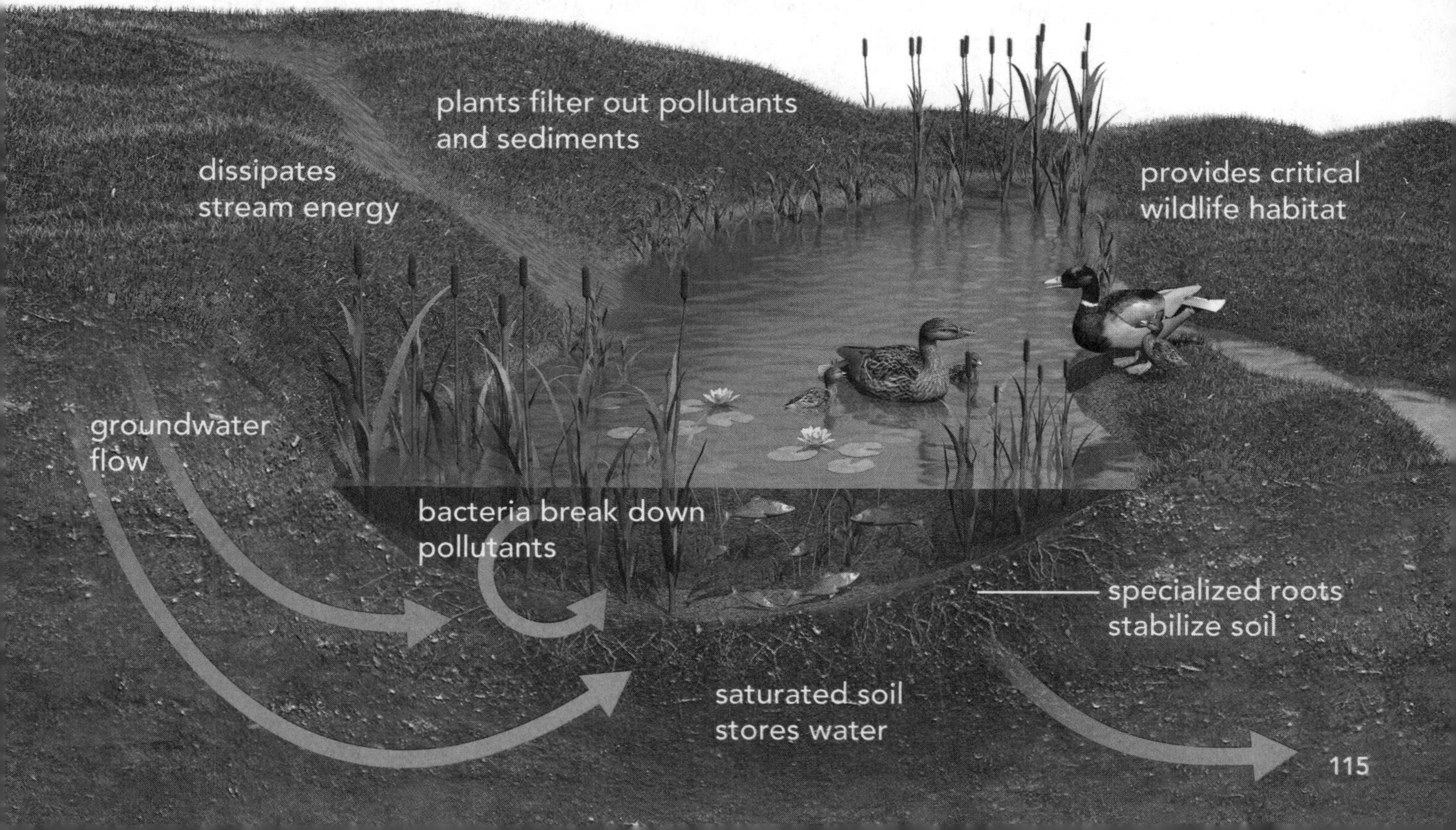

plants filter out pollutants and sediments

dissipates stream energy

provides critical wildlife habitat

groundwater flow

bacteria break down pollutants

specialized roots stabilize soil

saturated soil stores water

Sustainability

Figure 8 Examine the forest closely. Notice the amount of deforestation.

SEP Engage in Argument Do you think these trees are being managed in a way that maintains the overall health of the forest? Explain.

....

....

....

....

....

....

....

Sustainable Forest Management

Trees and other plants, like the ones in **Figure 8**, are important land resources. They provide food and shelter for many organisms. Through photosynthesis, they release oxygen into the air. They also absorb carbon dioxide and other pollutants from the air. Their roots absorb rainwater and hold the soil together, which helps to prevent erosion and flooding.

Many products are made from the fruit, seeds, and other parts of forest plants. The wood from some trees is used for making paper, and other trees are used to build homes and furniture. Fruits and seeds from trees provide food for people and animals.

All trees, whether cultivated by farmers or growing in the wild, need to be protected and managed sustainably. Because we can plant trees to replace trees that are cut down, forests can be renewable resources. How long a resource lasts depends on how people use it. **Sustainable** use of a resource means using it in ways that maintain the resource for all future generations. Replacing and reserving trees are important ways to sustain a forest. These practices ensure that the ecosystem remains healthy and that people can still depend on forests for the resources they need.

Logging Methods There are two main methods of logging, or cutting down trees: clear-cutting and selective cutting, illustrated in **Figure 9**. Clear-cutting is the process of cutting down all the trees in an area at once. Selective cutting is the process of cutting down only some trees in a forest and leaving a mix of tree sizes and species behind.

Clear-cutting is usually faster and less expensive than selective cutting. However, selective cutting is less damaging to the forest ecosystem than clear-cutting. When a forest is cleared, all the animals' habitats are suddenly gone. Without the protection of the trees, the soil is more easily eroded by wind and rain. The soil can then be blown or washed away and into nearby streams, harming aquatic ecosystems.

Selective cutting takes much longer, as the loggers need to actively choose which trees will come down and which will remain. It is more dangerous for loggers to selectively cut trees because they have to move heavy equipment and logs around the remaining trees.

Logging Methods
Figure 9 🖊 Clear-cutting and selective cutting are two methods of tree harvesting. Label each method shown as clear-cutting or selective cutting.

Original Forest

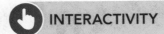

INTERACTIVITY

Create a solution for a controversial use of land.

Write About It Collect information about how trees in your state are managed. In your science notebook, write an argument from the position of a conservation organization that says the yield is too high and needs to be reduced.

Conserving Forest Habitats

Figure 10 Conserving forests can also help endangered species. The California condor is the most endangered species in the world, with fewer than 450 individuals alive. This four-foot-tall, 25-pound bird can fly 100 miles a day looking for dead animals to scavenge from, so it needs large, continuous forests.

Sustainable Forestry Forests can be managed to provide a sustainable yield. A sustainable yield is the amount of a renewable resource that can be harvested regularly without reducing the future supply. Planting one tree to replace each one that is cut down ensures that the overall yield remains constant.

In sustainable forestry, after trees are harvested, young trees are planted, as shown in **Figure 10**. Trees must be planted frequently enough to maintain a constant supply. Forests containing fast-growing tree species, such as pines, can be harvested and replanted every 20 to 30 years. Forests containing slower-growing species, such as hickory, oak, and cherry, may be harvested only every 40 to 100 years. One sustainable approach is to log small patches within a forest, so different sections can be harvested every year.

CHECK POINT **Draw Evidence** Why is it important to manage forests so that their yield is sustainable?

....

....

....

....

....

....

MS-ESS3-4

1. **Communicate** What are three different ways land is used as a resource?

....

....

2. **SEP Cite Evidence** Why are trees considered a renewable resource?

....

....

....

3. **Construct Arguments** How do poor farming methods impact Earth?

....

....

....

....

....

....

....

4. **SEP Evaluate Evidence** Give evidence to defend the claim that it is environmentally unsound to change the flow of water in a wetland.

....

....

....

....

....

....

....

....

5. **CCC Cause and Effect** How does the presence of trees maintain the stability of land resources?

....

....

....

....

....

Quest CHECK-IN

In this lesson, you learned about natural resources found on land and their importance to Earth's systems. You also learned how humans positively and negatively affect these resources.

SEP Evaluate Evidence Why is it important to conserve resources and not simply use them in the most convenient way?

....

....

....

....

....

👆 **INTERACTIVITY**

Life of a Landfill

Go online to learn about where to site a landfill and how a landfill is constructed.

 Water Pollution

 HANDS-ON LAB

uInvestigate Practice different techniques for cleaning up oil spills.

 MS-ESS3-4 Construct an argument supported by evidence for how increases in human population and per-capita consumption of natural resources impact Earth's systems.

Connect It !

 Circle the areas in the photo that contain fresh water.

SEP Provide Evidence Why is water an important resource?

....

....

Water as a Resource

Water is essential for life on Earth. Most of Earth's surface is covered by some form of water, as shown in **Figure 1**. It serves as a habitat for many species. Approximately 97 percent of the water on Earth is undrinkable because it contains salt. Of the remaining 3 percent, most is frozen solid in the polar ice sheets. That leaves less than 1 percent of all the water on the planet as drinkable.

Earth's water is a renewable resource, but fresh water is a limited resource. Recall that water continually moves between the atmosphere and Earth's surface in the water cycle. However, there is not always enough water in a given place at a given time. When water usage is poorly managed, it can lead to water shortages.

The limited supply of fresh water is not evenly **distributed** around the world. Some areas have an abundant supply, while in others it is quite scarce. Water scarcity occurs when there is not enough water to meet demand. It can be caused by droughts, low levels of groundwater, unequal water distribution, or environmental factors such as water pollution. An area faces water scarcity when the water supply is less than 1,000 cubic meters per person.

☑ CHECK POINT **Draw Evidence** Why is water a limited resource even though it is renewable?

....

....

Reflect What do you think the world's freshwater supply will look like in another 100 years? In your science notebook, describe how and why our water supply might change.

Academic Vocabulary

What are some items that might get distributed? Can you think of any examples from your school?

....

....

Fresh Water

Figure 1 In this image of Marsh Lake in Fresno County, California, fresh water may seem abundant. But drinkable fresh water makes up less than one percent of the water on Earth.

Water Pollution

Figure 2 Most sources of freshwater pollution come from human activities.

1. **Claim** ✏ Mark any examples of nonpoint sources of pollution with a check mark. Mark any examples of point sources of pollution with an X.

2. **Evidence** What evidence did you use to identify your claims?

....

....

3. **Reasoning** Explain how your evidence supports your claim.

....

....

....

....

....

....

Sources of Freshwater Pollution

Since fresh water is so limited, any pollution entering the water supply can have drastic short or long-term consequences. Most water pollution is directly linked to human activities, as shown in **Figure 2**. Wastes from farming, households, industry, and mining can end up in the water supply. Water pollutants may be point or nonpoint sources, depending on how they enter the water. A point source for water pollution could be a factory output pipe or a leaking landfill. Nonpoint pollution sources could be farm pesticides, farm animal wastes, or runoff of salt and chemicals from roads.

Farming Wastes
Animal wastes, fertilizers, and pesticides are sources of pollution. When it rains, pollutants can run off into nearby water sources and eventually the ocean. Wastes and fertilizers can cause overgrowths of algae. The algae block light and their decomposing remains deplete the water of oxygen, killing everything in the water.

Household Pollutants
The water and human wastes that are washed down sinks, showers, and toilets are called **sewage**. Sometimes, the sewage can leak into groundwater before it is treated. Because sewage contains many disease-causing bacteria, people will become ill if they drink or swim in water containing it.

Industrial Wastes
The waste products of factories and mines may also pollute the water. Many manufacturing processes use or produce toxic chemicals that need to be disposed of properly. During this disposal, chemicals sometimes leak into the groundwater. Some chemicals, such as heavy metals, build up in the bodies of aquatic organisms, making them and the animals that eat them ill.

Sediment
Erosion carries small particles of rocks and sand from the land into the water. These particles are called **sediment**. Sediment can cover up sources of food, nests, and eggs of aquatic organisms. Sediment also blocks sunlight, which prevents photosynthesis in plants.

Heat
When heat negatively affects bodies of water, it is known as **thermal pollution**. Factories and power plants use water to cool their machinery. This heated water is often discharged back into the environment. Because it is so hot, the water can kill organisms.

Oil and Gasoline
Oil and gasoline are often transported in long pipelines, either underground or above ground. Sometimes these pipelines leak into rivers, streams, or groundwater. When oil and gasoline pollute the water, it can take many years for the ecosystem to recover. Oil is difficult to collect and penetrates much of the soil in the area. It also affects the plants that grow along the water's edge. Spilled oil also has both direct and indirect effects on wildlife. Directly, it coats their fur or feathers and may cause skin irritations. Indirectly, oil may kill their source of food.

Oil and gasoline leaks from underground storage tanks are also sources of water pollution. These leaks can seep into the groundwater, making it unfit to drink.

✓ CHECK POINT **Draw Evidence** Does most water pollution happen as a result of human activities? Explain.

....

....

....

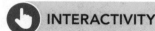 INTERACTIVITY

Examine how pollution affects the water cycle.

Literacy Connection

Draw Evidence Sometimes you need to draw evidence to support your analysis of a certain topic. Reread the previous page and the current page. As you read, underline any pieces of evidence that support the idea that most water pollution is directly linked to human activities.

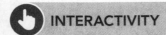
INTERACTIVITY

Investigate whether or not human activity is responsible for odd mutations found in frogs.

Sources of Ocean Pollution

It was once thought that "the solution to pollution is dilution." This meant that whatever was dumped into the ocean would just spread out and eventually go away. Today, we know that isn't true. Dumping large amounts of wastes into the ocean threatens marine organisms and the overall functioning of Earth's systems.

Natural Occurrences There are some "pollutants" that occur naturally. These include unpolluted freshwater runoff from land after heavy rains. When this fresh water enters the ocean, the salinity drops. Some organisms cannot tolerate this, so they either move to saltier waters or die.

Human Activities Most ocean pollution is related to human activities. The chemicals, sewage, and other wastes that are dumped into the ocean come from human sources. Fertilizers and pesticides from farms run off and eventually make it to the ocean. When enough of these build up, they can create an ocean dead zone—an area where nothing can live because there is not enough oxygen in the water.

Trash Trash and plastic, as shown in **Figure 3**, are hazardous to marine animals. For example, sea turtles often mistake plastic bags floating in the water for jellyfish. Once consumed, the bags clog up the intestines of the turtles. Fishing line and nets can catch swimming animals and entangle them. One area in the Pacific Ocean contains about 2 million bits of plastic per square mile. When sea creatures consume these tiny pieces, they can become ill and die. The plastic bits can also cause health problems for animals higher up in the food chain that eat small animals with plastic inside of them.

Effects of Pollution

Figure 3 This plastic and trash was recovered from the ocean, where it can harm organisms.

SEP Design Solutions
What are some ways humans can reduce the amount of plastic that ends up in the ocean?

....

....

....

....

Sources of Oil Pollution

There are different ways for oil to pollute the ocean.

1. **Construct Graphs** ✎ Create a bar graph of the data.

2. **Analyze Proportional Relationships** The amount of pollution caused by land runoff is greater than that caused by oil spills. Use ratios to describe how much greater land runoff pollution is than oil spill pollution.

....

Source of Oil Pollution	Oil Pollution (millions of liters)
Offshore drilling	80
Land runoff	1,375
Natural seeps	240
Ship repair	510
Oil spills	125

Oil Spills Oil that is accidentally spilled into the ocean is also a large source of pollution. Oil rigs that drill for oil sometimes leak into the ocean. This oil coats the feathers of birds, reducing their ability to stay warm. Oil also harms animals if they swallow it. Pollutants can build up in organisms' bodies and poison people or other marine life that feed on them.

 VIDEO

Explore the misconception that the ocean cannot be harmed because it is so vast.

Aquaculture The practice of raising fish and other water-dwelling organisms for food is called aquaculture. Fish are often raised in artificial ponds and bays that replace and destroy natural habitats, such as salt marshes. The farms can cause pollution and spread diseases into wild fish populations.

☑ CHECK POINT **Determine Conclusions** How can you help to reduce the amount of pollution that ends up in the ocean?

....

....

....

....

HANDS-ON LAB

Investigate Practice different techniques for cleaning up oil spills.

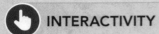

INTERACTIVITY

Take a closer look at water pollution and solutions.

Refugio Oil Spill
Figure 4 In 2015, an oil pipeline off the coast of southern California ruptured. Over 140,000 gallons of crude oil spilled into the ocean and washed up onto the shores of Santa Barbara.

Reducing Water Pollution

Everyone needs clean water. But how can the pollution that currently enters the water be reduced, and what efforts can be made to prevent future pollution?

The United States and other countries have laws that regulate water-polluting substances. These laws mandate the types and amounts of substances that can be dumped into the water. While these laws help, the keys to keeping water clean are the prevention of oil and gasoline spills, effective cleanup of spills, proper sewage treatment, and reduction of pollutants.

Protecting the Ocean The ocean is a continuous body of water. Because no one country owns the ocean, it is every nation's responsibility to do whatever it can to ensure the water stays clean. To help protect the ocean, the United Nations set up regulations that say the first 22 kilometers from the coast are controlled by the nation that owns that coast. That nation also controls any resources, such as oil, natural gas, and fish, that are found out to 370 km.

Many nations are helping to protect the ocean by limiting how much can be taken from it and by establishing marine protected areas (MPAs). They also are working to reduce the amount of pollution in their coastal waters.

Cleaning Oil Spills Oil spills, such as the one in **Figure 4**, are one of the worst environmental hazards that can occur. While nature can clean small amounts of oil from the water, large spills such as the Refugio oil spill are too much to handle. The bacteria that are able to digest oil cannot keep up with the volume of oil that is released in such a spill. Boats deploy skimming devices to collect floating oil, and barriers are set up to absorb or block oil before it reaches the shore. Chemical dispersants are also sprayed into the water to break up the oil. However, oil reached the west coast beaches, including Santa Barbara. Cleanup of a major oil spill in the ocean can take many years.

Improved Farming Methods Modern farming practices reduce water pollution. Formerly, farmers would leave fields bare in winter, allowing soil and fertilizers to wash into streams. It was also common to use large amounts of pesticides, herbicides, and fungicides. These chemicals would run off into streams, polluting the water and killing organisms. Today, farmers can reduce erosion and pollution by leaving stalks in the field or planting winter grasses that hold the soil and nutrients in place. Farmers also treat their land with a smaller amount of chemicals, and find natural predators to combat pests.

Reducing Pollutants Another way to protect Earth's waters is to reduce the amount of pollution that is created. Instead of dumping waste products directly into the environment, manufacturers can recycle them. By turning waste products into new things, the companies may even save money. Another method to reduce waste is to change the way materials are produced. Factories can eliminate the use of non-recyclable materials. By figuring out more environmentally-friendly manufacturing methods, they may make less total waste or less hazardous waste.

You can help to prevent water pollution in your home. Common household water pollutants include paints, paint thinner, motor oil, and garden chemicals. Instead of dumping these into the environment, save these materials for your community's hazardous waste collection day (**Figure 5**), or take them to a specialized facility for such wastes.

Hazardous Waste

Figure 5 Many towns and cities have special recycling centers that provide safe and proper disposal of household chemicals, such as paint and cleaning supplies.

✓ CHECK POINT **Write Explanatory Texts** What can your community do to reduce water pollution?

....

....

....

Plan It

Reducing Waste in Factories

Many factories are "going green" and changing the way they manufacture products to create less waste. Suppose there is a manufacturing company in your community that is not reducing its waste.

Construct Arguments Come up with a solution to your community's problem. Plan a presentation to convince the factory owners to "go green." How might changing their policy benefit both the community and the factory? How will making these changes impact the environment?

☑ LESSON 4 Check

MS-ESS3-4

1. SEP Construct Explanations Why is it so important for sources of fresh water to be protected?

....
....
....
....

2. CCC Cause and Effect How do farming methods cause water pollution?

....
....
....

3. SEP Provide Evidence What evidence suggests that factories sometimes cause water pollution?

....
....
....
....
....
....

4. CCC Analyze Systems How does water pollution in one area affect water and organisms elsewhere?

....
....
....
....
....
....

5. Construct Arguments Write an argument to defend the idea that oil spills are the worst environmental hazard.

....
....
....
....
....
....
....
....

Quest CHECK-IN

In this lesson, you learned why fresh water is a limited resource within Earth's systems. You also discovered how human activities lead to water pollution and how humans can reduce freshwater and ocean pollution.

CCC Analyze Systems Why is it important to consider the effects of waste disposal on water sources?

....
....
....

INTERACTIVITY

Reducing Waste

Go online to determine how everyone at your school can work together to reduce wastes and help the environment. Then make a plan to reduce the trash output at your school.

FROM WASTEWATER TO
Tap Water

▶ **VIDEO**

Walk through the water treatment process.

Fresh water is a precious resource on Earth, so we reuse every drop we can. Wastewater from homes and businesses ends up being recycled for irrigation, manufacturing, and replenishing aquatic ecosystems. But how do you recycle wastewater into drinking water? You engineer it!

The Challenge: To treat wastewater so it can return to the water supply.

Phenomenon In San Diego, California, the Point Loma Wastewater Treatment plant treats wastewater and makes it safe to drink, but it takes several steps. First, water from the sewer system passes through screens that filter out large particles. Next, the water flows into tanks where gravity separates solid waste from the water. Heavy solids sink to the bottom.

The water then flows to a second set of tanks where bacteria digest waste that's still in the water. Then the water is left to settle one more time and the last sediments are removed.

Following that, the water goes through a series of filters to get rid of any small solids or harmful microorganisms. The last step is disinfection using chlorine and UV light. Finally, this water will spend about six months in storage before it arrives at a tap.

DESIGN CHALLENGE

Can you design a model for recycling wastewater or rainwater from your home or school? Go to the Engineering Design Notebook to find out!

A typical wastewater plant has many, many tanks.

Primary Treatment			**Secondary Treatment**		**Disinfection**		
Pumping station	Primary screening	Primary sedimentation	Bacteria treatment	Secondary sedimentation	Filtration for micro-organisms	Cleaning with chlorine and UV	Clean water

Wastewater

MS-ESS3-4

Lange's metalmark butterfly

Evidence-Based Assessment

In 1976, ecologists made a disturbing discovery in the Antioch Dunes along the banks of the San Joaquin River in San Francisco, California. A butterfly, formally observed first in 1939 and only found in the dunes, was going extinct. Known as Lange's metalmark butterfly, it became one of the first insects protected as an endangered species by federal law.

Here are some important facts about the butterfly and its habitat:

- Lange's metalmark butterfly produces one crop of offspring each year. Females only lay their eggs on one species of plant, the naked-stem buckwheat plant.

- The dunes where the butterfly lives formed thousands of years ago, when sand deposited by ancient glaciers was moved and shaped by water and wind.

- When the first American settlers arrived in the early 1800s, the dunes ran along the river for about 3 kilometers (2 miles) and reached over 30 meters (100 feet) high in some places.

- As the human population of San Francisco grew, parts of the dunes were leveled and developed for industry. Sand from the dunes was mined to produce bricks and other building materials. The data table shows changes in the human population of San Francisco from 1850 to 2000.

San Francisco County Population, 1850–2000			
Year	Population	Year	Population
1850	21,000	1930	634,394
1860	56,802	1940	634,536
1870	149,473	1950	775,357
1880	233,959	1960	740,316
1890	298,997	1970	715,674
1900	342,782	1980	678,974
1910	416,912	1990	723,959
1920	506,676	2000	776,733

1. **SEP Analyze Data** Which statement about the trends in San Francisco's population growth is valid?

    A. It dropped for a few decades after 1890, but has grown almost every year since then.

    B. It grew slowly each year until 1930, when the population quickly increased.

    C. It increased steadily each decade from the 1850s to the 1950s.

    D. It grew rapidly in the mid to late 1800s and then again in the 1940s.

2. **CCC Cause and Effect** How has mining and extracting sand affected plants that live in the dunes, like the naked-stem buckwheat? Order the events from 1 to 4, with 1 being the first event and 4 being the final event.

Fewer plants like the buckwheat are able to survive due to lack of resources.	_____
The population of San Francisco grows dramatically between 1940 and 1950.	_____
A lot of sand is removed from the dunes.	_____
More pepole require land for roads, homes, and buildings.	_____

3. **Apply Scientific Reasoning** The remaining sand dunes became a national wildlife refuge in 1980. A few years later, researchers began an annual count of the butterflies. Between 1999 and 2008, the number of butterflies fell steadily. What might account for this continued drop?

    ....

    ....

    ....

    ....

    ....

4. **SEP Engage in Argument** How could an increase in the human population of San Francisco have impacted the Lange's metalmark butterflies that lived there? Use evidence from the text to support your answer.

    ....

    ....

    ....

    ....

    ....

    ....

    ....

    ....

    ....

    ....

    ....

Quest FINDINGS

Complete the Quest!

Phenomenon Refine your plan to reduce trash at your school and present the plan.

CCC Cause and Effect We produce a lot of trash that is disposed of in landfills. How would decreasing the trash we generate affect Earth's systems?

....

....

....

....

👆 **INTERACTIVITY**

Reflect on Trash Backlash

MS-ESS3-4

Washing Away

Background

Phenomenon A nearby town is considering a developer's plan to turn riverfront property into shops, restaurants, and apartments. The area is now an undisturbed habitat consisting of trees, bushes, and grasses. Almost all of the natural vegetation will be removed during construction. You will be part of a team tasked with providing an environmental impact report to the town board.

In this lab, you will design and conduct an investigation into the impact of vegetation and ground cover on soil erosion. You will test how quickly water runs off soil in different conditions and how much soil is carried away by the water.

How can you demonstrate the impact of **human activity** on **soil erosion?**

Materials

(per group)
- two 2-liter beverage bottles, cut lengthwise to form troughs
- about 4 cups of potting soil, divided in half
- grass or radish seedlings
- 2 large plastic cups
- 1 liter of water
- watering can with rain spout
- stopwatch

Plan Your Investigation

☐ 1. Work with your partner to design an experimental setup using the materials provided by your teacher. Your experiment must test how fast water runs off the soil and how much soil is carried away in the runoff. As you design your setup, consider the following questions:

- How would you describe the condition of the riverbank before the proposed construction?

- How would you describe the condition of the riverbank during the construction?

- How can you use the materials to model the condition of the riverbank before and during construction?

- How can you design your setup so that you will be able to measure how fast the water runs off the soil and how much soil is contained in the runoff?

- What are your dependent variable and independent variable, and the factors you hold constant?

- How many tests will you run?

- What observations will you make and what data will you collect?

☐ 2. Write a detailed procedure describing how you will investigate the effects of removing vegetation and ground cover on soil erosion. Include any sketches of your setup.

☐ 3. After getting teacher approval for your procedure, conduct your investigation.

☐ 4. Record your observations and data in the table provided.

Demonstrate Go online for a downloadable worksheet of this lab.

uDemonstrate Lab

Procedure and Sketches

Data Table

Bottle	Water Poured (mL)	Water Captured (mL)	Time (sec)	Observations of Water Collected
Grass and soil				
Soil only				

Analyze and Interpret Data

1. Compare Data Review the data you collected and the observations you recorded. How do the results of your tests compare?

....

....

....

....

2. Write an Expression Suppose you were going to graph the results of your investigation. How would you express the independent variable *Water Poured* as a variable? How would you express the results of your dependent variable *Water Captured* as a variable?

....

....

3. Apply Scientific Reasoning Based on the results of your investigation, describe how soil erosion might affect the ecology of rivers, lakes, and other bodies of water.

....

....

....

....

4. Refine Your Plan Examine and evaluate the procedures of other teams. Based on what you learned, how might you modify your own procedure to improve the results of your investigation?

....

....

....

....

....

5. SEP Engage in Argument What would you recommend to the town board? Use data from your investigation as evidence to justify your claim.

....

....

....

....

....

MS-ESS3-4, EP&CIIa, EP&CIIb,
EP&CIVb, EP&CVa, EP&CVb

Nothing Goes TO WASTE

One city in Texas is making sure nothing in its sewers goes to waste. The Hornsby Bend Biosolids Management Plant in Austin, Texas, recycles sewage into biosolids. Biosolids are rich in nutrients, so they make great soil and fertilizer.

Every day, Hornsby Bend receives about a million gallons of sewage solids from Austin's water treatment plants, where the sewage is separated from the wastewater. The sewage is screened, and then flows into tanks where bacteria get to work feeding on it. The bacteria break the sewage down, killing most disease organisms as they go. This process is actually not that different from how the human digestive system works. After about 60 days, the sewage is converted into biosolids.

Hornsby Bend also collects Austin's yard trimmings and mixes these with the biosolids to make nutrient-rich soil. The plant sends some soil to nearby farmers who enhance their existing soil with the mix. The rest is used to supplement the soil of Austin's public lawns, gardens, parks, and golf courses. Instead of going to an expensive landfill, the biosolids are put to good use.

Hornsby Bend is also a bird sanctuary with more than 350 types of birds.

All of the water used at the treatment plant is recycled, too. Some of it goes to irrigate the nearby farmland, and the rest goes to ponds at the treatment plant. The nutrient-rich pond water has still another benefit: the treatment plant is also a bird sanctuary. Hornsby Bend is one of the best birding sites in the state. Thanks to the Hornsby Bend Biosolids Management Plant, Austin's waste doesn't go to waste.

Use the table to answer the following questions.

1. **CCC Scale, Proportion, and Quantity** One sample of biosolids contains 18.2 mg/kg mercury, 22.5 mg/kg arsenic, and 29.7 mg/kg cadmium. Are these biosolids safe to use? Why or why not?

   ....

   ....

2. **SEP Use Mathematics** A biosolids plant is picking up waste from a new factory. The level of lead in the plant's biosolids had been 121 mg/kg. With the waste from the new factory, the lead has increased 12 percent. Calculate the new lead level to determine if the biosolid is still safe to use on farmland.

   ....

   ....

   ....

3. **Connect to Society** Why is a chart like this important?

   ....

   ....

   ....

4. **SEP Engage in Argument** Are biosolids safe to use in agriculture? Make an argument to support your answer.

   ....

   ....

   ....

   ....

Safe Levels of Pollutants in Soil on Farms Fertilized with Biosolids	
Pollutant	Risk Assessment Acceptable Soil Concentration (mg/kg-soil)
Arsenic	23.5
Cadmium	19.7
Copper	769.0
Lead	161.0
Mercury	8.6
Nickel	228.0
Selenium	50.21
Zinc	1,454.0

SOURCE: Environmental Protection Agency

MS-ESS3-4, EP&CIa, EP&CIc,
EP&CIIa, EP&CIIb, EP&CIIc,
EP&CIVa, EP&CIVb, EP&CIVc

Is Plastic Really So Fantastic?

Chemists use crude oil to make plastics in a lab.

Look around your classroom or community, and you will likely see many things made from plastic.

Most plastic is synthesized from petroleum, or crude oil. This natural resource is a mixture of thousands of different compounds. To make plastic from it, these compounds have to be processed.

Oil is a mixture of carbon and hydrogen atoms, which differ in size and structure. These atoms form simple monomers. Through several chemical reactions, the monomers form large chains of polymers, and you end up with plastic.

The Benefits of Plastic

Plastic has had a profound impact on society. It is very durable and fairly inexpensive to produce. Plastic is much lighter than metal, and it can be molded into just about any shape. These properties work to our advantage in a wide variety of applications. Many auto parts are plastic because they increase fuel efficiency by decreasing the mass of the car.

The Drawbacks of Plastic

While plastic is a world-changing synthetic material, it has its share of problems. Plastic materials do not biodegrade readily. Landfills are overflowing with plastic items that will be around for many hundreds of years. Plastic refuse also has ended up in the oceans, impacting the survival of fish and other aquatic organisms.

One way to deal with the negative impacts of plastics is to recycle as much of it as possible. The table shows how the recycling of different types of plastic bottles has changed from 2013 to 2014.

Postconsumer Plastics Recycled in U.S., 2013–2014		
Plastic Bottle Type	**Plastic Recycled (millions of pounds)**	**Recycling Rate**
2013 PET	1798	31.2%
HDPE Natural	440.4	28.0%
HDPE Pigmented	605.0	34.9%
Total Bottles	1045.4	31.6%
2014 PET	1812	31.0%
HDPE Natural	464.4	29.9%
HDPE Pigmented	643.0	36.8%
Total Bottles	1107.4	33.6%

Use the table to answer the following questions.

1. CCC Patterns What patterns do you observe among the data in the table?

2. SEP Use Mathematics What do you think the recycling data will look like in 2020? Explain. Do a calculation that predicts what the percentage will be.

3. SEP Plan an Investigation Describe an experiment that could be conducted to investigate how long it takes different plastics to break down.

4. CCC Cause and Effect What are some ways you can think of to get people to recycle more plastic instead of allowing it to end up in a landfill or the ocean?

Take Notes

Use this space for recording notes and sketching out ideas.

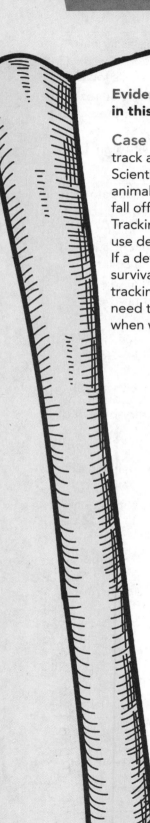

Evidence Now that you have completed the three topics in this segment, do the following tasks.

Case Study There are some challenges in using collars to track animals. Trapping and collaring an animal can be difficult. Scientists may use traps, tranquilizers, and nets to capture an animal. Collars must fit properly or they could hurt the animal, fall off, restrict movement, or interfere with the animal's behavior. Tracking devices also require a power source. Scientists try to use devices that weigh less than 5% of an animal's body weight. If a device is too heavy, it will impact the animal's behavior and survival, and thus interfere with the study. When choosing a tracking method, scientists must consider the type of data they need to collect, along with any constraints they may encounter when working with the animal in its habitat.

The North American river otter spends time on land and in the water. River otters are typically three to four feet long and weigh between 7 and 14 kilograms. They can dive to a depth of 1.5 meters and can swim up to 11 kilometers per hour. River otters are active all year round.

Collaborative Conversations Suppose you are a scientist who wants to develop a conservation plan for the North American river otter in the San Francisco Bay area. Working with a partner, discuss how you could you learn more about the river otter populations living there.

1. **SEP Plan an Investigation** What is the purpose of your research project?

....

....

....

....

2. **Identify Criteria** What data do you want to collect about the river otter?

....

....

....

3. **Identify Constraints** What might be some challenges in working with river otters in the wild?

....

....

....

Compare Tracking Devices

Type of Device	Advantages	Disadvantages
VHF	• collars cost $250 • easy to use and accurate • can be used on a variety of animals • battery can last up to three years • visual sightings allow data to be collected on home range, habitat usage, behavior, diet, and population	• need to receive transmitter signals from at least three different locations to identify animal's location • human interference, as it requires a person in the field to track the signal and record data • weather can interfere with signal
GPS	• most GPS collars also have VHF capabilities, so animals can be tracked and behaviors observed • provides large amounts of animal location data • highly accurate • data can be collected in person, transmitted by mobile phone technology, or downloaded remotely • batteries last around 2 years • less human interference	• collars cost $1,500 (manual data download) to $4,000 (remote data download) • needs more power to function, which adds to the weight of the collar • mobile phone signal is limited in some areas, so data cannot be transmitted • may require personnel in the field to retrieve the collar or be nearby to collect the data • landscape can interfere with signal
Satellite	• requires no personnel to collect data • can track long-range movement • can send data via e-mail • ideal for use in inaccessible areas • battery lasts around 2 years • less human interference	• collars cost $2,500 (battery-powered) to $3,000 (solar-powered) • less accurate • limited ability to gather behavioral data • landscape can interfere with signal

4. **SEP Analyze Data** Based on the data table, which device do you think is better suited to your research study? Why?

....

....

5. **SEP Conduct an Investigation** As part of planning your research study, you need to determine how many river otters you will track, for how long, and how often you will collect data. Use this information to describe the steps you will take to study the river otters.

....

....

....

....

....

Use what you have learned to answer the following questions.

1. **CCC Structure and Function** Do the properties and behaviors of waves change as they move through water or the atmosphere? Explain what impact this might have on tagging an animal that spends time on land and in the water.

....

....

....

....

....

2. **SEP Engage in Argument** Do advances in communication and information technologies help or harm biodiversity?

....

....

....

....

3. **SEP Design Solutions** Consider the types of tracking technologies that are available to you for your river otter study. The team studying pumas at the University of California had to develop a new device, the SMART collar, to obtain the data they needed. Design an improved tracking device that can work on the river otter. Sketch your design in the space provided. Label the parts and list why that feature is important.

Safety Symbols

These symbols warn of possible dangers in the laboratory and remind you to work carefully.

 Safety Goggles Wear safety goggles to protect your eyes in any activity involving chemicals, flames or heating, or glassware.

 Lab Apron Wear a laboratory apron to protect your skin and clothing from damage.

 Breakage Handle breakable materials, such as glassware, with care. Do not touch broken glassware.

 Heat-Resistant Gloves Use an oven mitt or other hand protection when handling hot materials, such as hot plates or hot glassware.

 Plastic Gloves Wear disposable plastic gloves when working with harmful chemicals and organisms. Keep your hands away from your face, and dispose of the gloves according to your teacher's instructions.

 Heating Use a clamp or tongs to pick up hot glassware. Do not touch hot objects with your bare hands.

 Flames Before you work with flames, tie back loose hair and clothing. Follow your teacher's instructions about lighting and extinguishing flames.

 No Flames When using flammable materials, make sure there are no flames, sparks, or other exposed heat sources present.

 Corrosive Chemical Avoid getting acid or other corrosive chemicals on your skin or clothing or in your eyes. Do not inhale the vapors. Wash your hands after the activity.

 Poison Do not let any poisonous chemical come into contact with your skin, and do not inhale its vapors. Wash your hands when you are finished with the activity.

 Fumes Work in a well-ventilated area when harmful vapors may be involved. Avoid inhaling vapors directly. Test an odor only when directed to do so by your teacher, and use a wafting motion to direct the vapor toward your nose.

 Sharp Object Scissors, scalpels, knives, needles, pins, and tacks can cut your skin. Always direct a sharp edge or point away from yourself and others.

 Animal Safety Treat live or preserved animals or animal parts with care to avoid harming the animals or yourself. Wash your hands when you are finished with the activity.

 Plant Safety Handle plants only as directed by your teacher. If you are allergic to certain plants, tell your teacher; do not do an activity involving those plants. Avoid touching harmful plants such as poison ivy. Wash your hands when you are finished with the activity.

 Electric Shock To avoid electric shock, never use electrical equipment around water, when the equipment is wet, or when your hands are wet. Be sure cords are untangled and cannot trip anyone. Unplug equipment not in use.

 Physical Safety When an experiment involves physical activity, avoid injuring yourself or others. Alert your teacher if there is any reason you should not participate.

 Disposal Dispose of chemicals and other laboratory materials safely. Follow the instructions from your teacher.

 Hand Washing Wash your hands thoroughly when finished with an activity. Use soap and warm water. Rinse well.

 General Safety Awareness When this symbol appears, follow the instructions provided. When you are asked to develop your own procedure in a lab, have your teacher approve your plan.

GLOSSARY

A

absolute age The age of a rock given as the number of years since the rock formed.

absorption The transfer of energy from a wave to a material that it encounters.

acceleration The rate at which velocity changes.

acid rain Rain or another form of precipitation that is more acidic than normal, caused by the release of molecules of sulfur dioxide and nitrogen oxide into the air.

adaptation An inherited behavior or physical characteristic that helps an organism survive and reproduce in its environment.

amphibian A vertebrate whose body temperature is determined by the temperature of its environment, and that lives its early life in water and its adult life on land.

amplitude The height of a transverse wave from the center to a crest or trough.

analog signal A signal that allows for a continuous record of some kind of action.

artificial selection The process by which humans breed only those organisms with desired traits to produce the next generation; selective breeding.

asteroid One of the rocky objects revolving around the sun that is too small and numerous to be considered a planet.

astronomical unit A unit of distance equal to the average distance between Earth and the sun, about 150 million kilometers.

autosomal chromosomes The 22 pairs of chromosomes that are not sex chromosomes.

axis An imaginary line that passes through a planet's center and its north and south poles, about which the planet rotates.

B

bandwidth The amount of information that can be transmitted in bits per second.

birth rate The number of people born per 1,000 individuals for a certain period of time.

C

chromosome A threadlike structure within a cell's nucleus that contains DNA that is passed from one generation to the next.

clone An organism that is genetically identical to the organism from which it was produced.

comet A loose collection of ice and dust that orbits the sun, typically in a long, narrow orbit.

competition The struggle between organisms to survive as they attempt to use the same limited resources in the same place at the same time.

concave A mirror with a surface that curves inward or a lens that is thinner at the center than at the edges.

conductor A material that allows electric charges to flow.

conservation The practice of using less of a resource so that it can last longer.

constellation A pattern or grouping of stars that people imagine to represent a figure or object.

convex A mirror that curves outward or lens that is thicker in the center than at the edges.

D

death rate The number of deaths per 1,000 individuals in a certain period of time.

decibel (dB) A unit used to compare the loudness of different sounds.

deforestation The removal of forests to use the land for other reasons.

diffraction The bending or spreading of waves as they move around a barrier or pass through an opening.

diffuse reflection Reflection that occurs when parallel light rays hit an uneven surface and all reflect at different angles.

digital signal A signal that allows for a record of numerical values of an action at a set of continuous time intervals.

Doppler effect The change in frequency of a wave as its source moves in relation to an observer.

E

eclipse The partial or total blocking of one object in space by another.

elastic potential energy The energy associated with objects that can be compressed or stretched.

electric current The continuous flow of electrical charges through a material.

electric field The region around a charged object where the object's electric force is exerted on other charged objects.

electric force The force between charged objects.

electric motor A device that transforms electrical energy to mechanical energy.

electromagnet A magnet created by wrapping a coil of wire with a current running through it around a core of material that is easily magnetized.

electromagnetic induction The process of generating an electric current from the motion of a conductor through a magnetic field.

electromagnetic signal Information that is sent as a pattern of electromagnetic waves, such as visible light, microwaves, and radio waves.

electromagnetism The relationship between electricity and magnetism.

electron A tiny particle that moves around the outside of the nucleus of an atom.

electronic signal Information that is sent as a pattern in a controlled flow of current through a circuit.

ellipse An oval shape, which may be elongated or nearly circular; the shape of the planets' orbits.

embryo The young organism that develops from a zygote.

emissions Pollutants that are released into the air.

energy The ability to cause change.

equinox Either of the two days of the year on which neither hemisphere is tilted toward or away from the sun.

era One of the three long units of geologic time between the Precambrian and the present.

erosion The process by which water, ice, wind, or gravity moves weathered particles of rock and soil.

evolution Change over time; the process by which modern organisms have descended from ancient organisms.

exponential growth A rate of change that increases more and more rapidly over time.

extinct Term used to refer to a group of related organisms that has died out and has no living members.

---------------- F ----------------

fitness How well an organism can survive and reproduce in its environment.

focal point The point at which light rays parallel to the optical axis meet, after being reflected (or refracted) by a mirror (or lens).

force A push or pull exerted on an object.

fossil The preserved remains or traces of an organism that lived in the past.

fossil record All the fossils that have been discovered and what scientists have learned from them.

frequency The number of complete waves that pass a given point in a certain amount of time.

friction The force that two surfaces exert on each other when they rub against each other.

---------------- G ----------------

galaxy A huge group of single stars, star systems, star clusters, dust, and gas bound together by gravity.

galvanometer A device that uses an electromagnet to detect small amounts of current.

gene therapy The process of replacing an absent or faulty gene with a normal working gene to treat a disease or medical disorder.

generator A device that transforms mechanical energy into electrical energy.

genetic engineering The transfer of a gene from the DNA of one organism into another organism, in order to produce an organism with desired traits.

genome The complete set of genetic information that an organism carries in its DNA.

geocentric Term describing a model of the universe in which Earth is at the center of the revolving planets and stars.

geologic time scale A record of the geologic events and life forms in Earth's history.

gravitational potential energy The potential energy related to an object's vertical position.

gravity The attractive force between objects; the force that moves objects downhill.

---------------- H ----------------

heliocentric Term describing a model of the solar system in which Earth and the other planets revolve around the sun.

homologous structures Structures that are similar in different species and that have been inherited from a common ancestor.

GLOSSARY

I

inertia The tendency of an object to resist a change in motion.

information technology Computer and telecommunication hardware and software that store, transmit, receive, and manipulate information.

intensity The amount of energy per second carried through a unit area by a wave.

interference The interaction between waves that meet.

invertebrate An animal without a backbone.

K

kinetic energy Energy that an object possesses by virtue of being in motion.

L

law of conservation of energy The law that states that energy is conserved. When one object loses energy, other objects must gain it.

law of superposition The geologic principle that states that in horizontal layers of sedimentary rock, each layer is older than the layer above it and younger than the layer below it.

law of universal gravitation The scientific law that states that every object in the universe attracts every other object.

longitudinal wave A wave that moves the medium in a direction parallel to the direction in which the wave travels.

loudness The perception of the energy of a sound.

M

magnet Any material that attracts iron and materials that contain iron.

magnetic field The region around a magnet where the magnetic force is exerted.

magnetic force A force produced when magnetic poles interact.

magnetic pole The ends of a magnetic object, where the magnetic force is strongest.

magnetism The force of attraction or repulsion of magnetic materials.

mammal A vertebrate whose body temperature is regulated by its internal heat, and that has skin covered with hair or fur and glands that produce milk to feed its young.

mass extinction When many types of living things become extinct at the same time.

maximum The greatest quantity or value attainable or attained.

mechanical wave A wave that requires a medium through which to travel.

mechanism The natural process by which something takes place.

medium The material through which a wave travels.

meteor A streak of light in the sky produced by the burning of a meteoroid in Earth's atmosphere.

meteoroid A chunk of rock or dust in space, generally smaller than an asteroid.

moon A natural satellite that orbits a planet.

motion The state in which one object's distance from another is changing.

mutation Any change in the DNA of a gene or a chromosome.

N

natural resource Anything naturally occurring in the environment that humans use.

natural selection The process by which organisms that are best adapted to their environment are most likely to survive and reproduce.

net force The overall force on an object when all the individual forces acting on it are added together.

newton A unit of measure that equals the force required to accelerate 1 kilogram of mass at 1 meter per second per second.

noise Random signals from the environment that can alter the output of a signal.

nonpoint source A widely spread source of pollution that is difficult to link to a specific point of origin.

nonrenewable resource A natural resource that is not replaced in a useful time frame.

O

opaque A type of material that reflects or absorbs all of the light that strikes it.

orbit The path of an object as it revolves around another object in space.

overpopulation A condition in which the number of humans grows beyond what the available resources can support.

ozone A form of oxygen that has three oxygen atoms in each molecule instead of the usual two; toxic to organisms where it forms near Earth's surface.

P

penumbra The part of a shadow surrounding the darkest part.

period One of the units of geologic time into which geologists divide eras.

phase One of the different apparent shapes of the moon as seen from Earth.

pitch A description of how a sound is perceived as high or low.

pixel A small, uniform shape that is combined with other pixels to make a larger image.

planet An object that orbits a star, is large enough to have become rounded by its own gravity, and has cleared the area of its orbit.

point source A specific source of pollution that can be identified.

pollution Contamination of Earth's land, water, or air through the release of harmful substances into the environment.

potential energy Stored energy based on position or shape of an object.

protein Large organic molecule made of carbon, hydrogen, oxygen, nitrogen, and sometimes sulfur.

R

radioactive dating The process of determining the age of an object using the half-life of one or more radioactive isotopes.

radioactive decay The process in which the nuclei of radioactive elements break down, releasing fastmoving particles and energy.

reference point A place or object used for comparison to determine whether an object is in motion.

reflection The bouncing back of an object or a wave when it hits a surface through which it cannot pass.

refraction The bending of waves as they enter a new medium at an angle, caused by a change in speed.

relative age The age of a rock compared to the ages of other rocks.

renewable resource A resource that is either always available or is naturally replaced in a relatively short time.

reptile A vertebrate whose temperature is determined by the temperature of its environment, that has lungs and scaly skin, and that lays eggs on land.

resonance The increase in the amplitude of a vibration that occurs when external vibrations match an object's natural frequency.

revolution The movement of an object around another object.

rotation The spinning motion of a planet on its axis.

S

satellite An object that orbits a planet.

scientific theory A well-tested explanation for a wide range of observations or experimental results.

sediment Small, solid pieces of material that come from rocks or the remains of organisms; earth materials deposited by erosion.

sewage The water and human wastes that are washed down sinks, toilets, and showers.

sex chromosomes The pair of chromosomes carrying genes that determine whether a person is biologically male or female.

sex-linked gene A gene carried on a sex chromosome.

slope The steepness of a graph line; the ratio of the vertical change (the rise) to the horizontal change (the run).

software Programs that encode, decode, and interpret information.

solar system The system consisting of the sun and the planets and other objects that revolve around it.

solenoid A coil of wire with a current.

solstice Either of the two days of the year on which the sun reaches its greatest distance north or south of the equator.

GLOSSARY

species A group of similar organisms that can mate with each other and produce offspring that can also mate and reproduce.

speed The distance an object travels per unit of time.

standing wave A wave that appears to stand in one place, even though it is two waves interfering as they pass through each other.

star A ball of hot gas, primarily hydrogen and helium, that undergoes nuclear fusion.

static electricity A buildup of charges on an object.

sun A large, gaseous body at the center of the solar system.

sustainable Using a resource in ways that maintain it at a certain quality for a certain period of time.

sustainable use The practice of allowing renewable resources time to recover and replenish.

T

telescope An optical instrument that forms enlarged images of distant objects.

thermal pollution A type of pollution caused by factories and power plants releasing superheated water into bodies of water.

transformer A device that increases or decreases voltage, which often consists of two separate coils of insulated wires wrapped around an iron core.

transluscent A type of material that scatters light as it passes through.

transparent A type of material that transmits light without scattering it.

transverse wave A wave that moves the medium at right angles to the direction in which the wave travels.

U

umbra The darkest part of a shadow.

unconformity A gap in the geologic record that shows where rock layers have been lost due to erosion.

V

variation Any difference between individuals of the same species.

velocity Speed in a given direction.

vertebrate An animal with a backbone.

virtue a capacity to act.

W

wave A disturbance that transfers energy from place to place.

wave pulse A pulse of energy that travels through an electric circuit when it is closed.

wavelength The distance between two corresponding parts of a wave, such as the distance between two crests.

weight A measure of the force of gravity acting on an object.

INDEX
Page numbers for key terms are printed in boldface type.

INDEX Page numbers for key terms are printed in boldface type.

CREDITS

Photography

Photo locators denoted as follows: Top (T), Center (C), Bottom (B), Left (L), Right (R), Background (Bkgd)

Covers

Front: Tntemerson/iStock/Getty Images; Rafe Swan/Getty Images; Stefan Christmann/Getty Images; Dudarev Mikhail/Shutterstock; Sumiko Scott/Getty Images; Back: Marinello/DigitalVision Vectors/Getty Images

Instructional Segment 4

iv Nick Lundgren/Shutterstock; vi: Steve Shuey/Alamy Stock Photo; vii: Raimundas/Shutterstock; viii: KPG Payless2/Shutterstock; x: Bkgrd: Brian J. Skerry/National Geographic/Getty Images; xT: Fabriziobalconi/Fotolia; ixB: Dale Kolke/ZUMA Press/Newscom; 000: Max Allen/Alamy Stock Photo; 002: Shah Selbe/Getty Images; 003CR: Stephen Osman/Los Angeles Times/Getty Images; 003B: Stephen Osman/Los Angeles Times/Getty Images; 005: Max Allen/Alamy Stock Photo; 006: U.S. Fish and Wildlife Service; 008: Steve Shuey/Alamy Stock Photo; 010: Mark Leary/Getty Images; 011: NOAA; 012: Wavebreak MediaLtd./123RF; 018: Rachid DahnounAurora Photos/Alamy Stock Photo; 019: Richard Megna/Fundamental Photographs; 021BL: Roberto Lo Savio/Shutterstock; 021BR: Nublee bin Shamsu Bahar/Shutterstock; 021BCL: Science Source; 021BCR: Kenny10/Shutterstock; 023: Denis Gladkiy/Fotolia; 025: Sergey Nivens/Fotolia; 027TR: Lionel Le Jeune/Fotolia; 027CR: Graham Oliver/123RF; 029: LightField Studios/Shutterstock; 030: Ron Thomas/Getty Images; 032T: Pukach/Shutterstock; 032C: Mike Flippo/Shutterstock; 032B: Andrey Kuzmin/Shutterstock; 033: Goran Djukanovic/Shutterstock; 034: Mr_sailor/iStock/Getty Images; 035: Vvoennyy/123RF; 039: Sirtravelalot/Shutterstock; 040: Yellow Cat/Shutterstock; 041C: Havoc/Shutterstock; 041B: Dibrova/Shutterstock; 042T: Tusharkoley/Shutterstock; 042B: Anne08/Shutterstock; 043T: TLF Design/Alamy Stock Photo; 043B: Yuelan/123RF; 044T: Science Source; 044B: Mediaphotos/iStock/Getty Images; 049TR: Blend Images/Alamy Stock Photo; 049B: Andrey Armyagov/123RF; 052: Joseph S. Giacalone/Alamy Stock Photo; 053: EpicStockMedia/Shutterstock; 056: Raimundas/Shutterstock; 058: Z2A1/Alamy Stock Photo; 060: Everett Collection/Shutterstock; 061TR: Pressmaster/Shutterstock; 061CR: Sirtravelalot/Shuttertock; 066: Susanne ommer/Shutterstock; 070: David H. Carriere/Getty Images; 072: Dotshock/Shutterstock; 074TCR: Gallofoto/Shutterstock; 074CR: Ruslan Ivantsov/Shutterstock; 074BL: Tempura/Getty Images; 075R: DAVID DUCROS/SCIENCE PHOTO LIBRARY/Getty Images; 075CR: Asharkyu/Shutterstock; 079: TeguhSantosa/Getty Images; 083TL: Doug Martin/Science Source; 083TR: Richard Megna/Fundamental Photographs; 086: KPG Payless2/Shutterstock; 088: National Geographic Creative/Alamy Stock Photo; 090: Justin Lambert/Getty Images; 095: Design Pics Inc/Alamy Stock Photo; 096: Kletr/Shutterstock; 098: Por Nahorski Pavel/Shutterstock; 102: Karol Kozlowski/Shutterstock; 104: Mark Kauzlarich/Bloomberg/Getty Images; 105: Science Source; 107: Chieko Hara/The Porterville Recorder/AP Images; 108: Jade Brookbank/Getty Images; 110BCL: Chad Ehlers/Alamy Stock Photo; 110BCR: Jiri Foltyn/Shutterstock; 110BR: Rob Crandall/Alamy Stock Photo; 111: Perytskyy/iStock/Getty Images; 112CL: Kletr/Shutterstock; 112CR: Blickwinkel/Alamy Stock Photo; 113: Tom Grundy/Alamy Stock Photo; 116: lowsun/Shutterstock; 118: Tom McHugh/Science Source; 120: iStock/Getty Images; 124: Rosanne Tackaberry/Alamy Stock Photo; 126: David McNew/Getty Images; 127: ZUMA Press Inc/Alamy Stock Photo; 132: Philipp Dase/Shutterstock; 141: Jouko van der Kruijssen/Getty Images.

Take Notes

Use this space for recording notes and sketching out ideas.

Use this space for recording notes and sketching out ideas.

Take Notes

Use this space for recording notes and sketching out ideas.

Take Notes

Use this space for recording notes and sketching out ideas.

Use this space for recording notes and sketching out ideas.

Take Notes

Use this space for recording notes and sketching out ideas.

Use this space for recording notes and sketching out ideas.

Take Notes

Use this space for recording notes and sketching out ideas.

Use this space for recording notes and sketching out ideas.

Take Notes

Use this space for recording notes and sketching out ideas.

Take Notes

Use this space for recording notes and sketching out ideas.

Take Notes

Use this space for recording notes and sketching out ideas.

Use this space for recording notes and sketching out ideas.

Take Notes

Use this space for recording notes and sketching out ideas.

Take Notes

Use this space for recording notes and sketching out ideas.

Take Notes

Use this space for recording notes and sketching out ideas.

Use this space for recording notes and sketching out ideas.

Take Notes

Use this space for recording notes and sketching out ideas.